start
me
up ™
special

MARS

By Wolfgang Engelhardt

Tessloff Publishing

Preface

For thousands of years humans have been fascinated by the planets they saw in the heavens. Mars, the "Red Planet," has always attracted a large share of this fascination. Its orbit around the Sun brings it close to the Earth approximately every other year.

With the invention of the telescope in the early 17th century, it became possible to study the planets more thoroughly. Not until the 1950's, however, with the beginnings of modern electronics and rocketry, did scientists have the means for more precise investigations. Now it was possible to send space probes to these distant planets and to explore them close up.

In 1964 the United States launched its first successful Mars probe, Mariner 4. The Mariner and Viking missions that followed were also very successful. The first probes just flew past Mars and on by into deep space. As they passed Mars they transmitted pictures of its surface and data about the surface and atmosphere. Soon more highly developed probes were able to enter into orbit around Mars and even send landing capsules down to the surface. Through these landing modules scientists were able to discover a wide variety of fascinating formations on the surface. These included Olympus Mons, a 17-mile-high volcano, and Valles Marineris, a canyon nearly 4 miles deep. The surface probes analyzed soil samples and collected data on the weather and climate on the Red Planet.

In recent years the "Mars rock" found in the Antarctic has caused a stir among researchers. Some scientists believe this rock from Mars contains traces of minute, primitive organisms that may have lived on Mars billions of years ago.

In mid-1997 the space probe Pathfinder landed on Mars and sent back spectacular pictures. This expedition was followed with great anticipation around the world. Pathfinder carried a vehicle that could travel on the planet's surface—the Sojourner rover. Scientists on Earth were able to steer this rover up to large rocks and to analyze their chemical composition.

This book describes these exciting missions to Mars, their goals, instruments, mission schedules, and results. Dozens of pictures illustrate what we have learned about Mars in the past few decades. The final section sketches the outlook for future Mars research and expeditions. It may not be as long as we imagine before we send a manned mission to the planet Mars.

start me up™ special

PUBLISHERS: Tessloff Publishing, Quadrillion Media LLC

EDITOR: Alan Swensen

PICTURE SOURCES:
COVER: Astrofoto, Leichlingen/NASA, van Ravenswaay. Wolfgang Engelhardt/Astro-Verlag, Cologne.
PHOTOS: Astrofoto, Leichlingen: 5, 18r, 21b, 55b. dpa, Frankfurt/Main: 6/7, 9.
NASA/JPL/RPIF/DLR/Wolfgang Engelhardt: 1, 7 – 19, 21 – 63.
ILLUSTRATIONS: Gerd Ohnesorge: 6. Uli Knauer: 4/5, 10, 16. Norbert Kühltau: 20.

Library of Congress Cataloging-in-Publication Data is available.

ISBN 1-58185-012-3

Printed in Belgium

Printing 10 9 8 7 6 5 4 3 2 1

Contents

Studying Mars—
an Exciting History

How does Mars compare to Earth?

Mars is the fourth of the Sun's satellites. It belongs to the group of planets that are similar to the Earth: it has a solid surface and is enveloped in a thin atmosphere. Since its surface is covered with iron oxide it appears red to us here on Earth, and has come to be known as the "Red Planet." The diameter of Mars averages 4,222 miles (6,793 km). This is about half as big as the Earth (7,927 miles or 12,757 km) and almost twice as big as the Moon (2,160 miles or 3,476 km).

Using Johannes Kepler's laws of physics, scientists long ago calculated the mass of Mars based on the length of its moons' orbits. The result was very precise: 7.2×10^{20} tons—almost exactly one tenth of the Earth's mass. If we relate this to the volume of Mars' sphere, we discover that Mars has an average density of 3.9 grams per cubic centimeter (g/cm^3). This means that Mars is about 4 times as heavy as a giant water-filled balloon of the same size would be. Still its density is less than the Earth's—Earth has a density of 5.5 g/cm^3—and as a result Mars' gravitational force isn't strong enough to hold more than a thin atmosphere around the planet. The atmosphere on Mars consists primarily of carbon dioxide—a gas that is poisonous for human beings.

Our solar system: an asteroid belt separates the four small inner planets, Mercury, Venus, Earth, and Mars, from the four outer planets, Saturn, Jupiter, Uranus, and Neptune, and from the smallest and most distant planet, Pluto.

Mars moves around the Sun in an elliptical, almost egg-shaped orbit. Its distance from the Sun thus varies from 154.8 to 128.4 million miles (250 to 207 million km). One complete orbit around the Sun—one "Mars year"—takes 687 Earth days. This is about twice as long as an Earth year (365 days). Centuries ago astronomers determined the time it took for Mars to rotate once around its own axis—one "Mars day." They used early telescopes and followed a recognizable dark spot on the planet's surface. It takes 24 hours and 37 minutes for one revolution—only 40 minutes longer than the Earth's rotation. In contrast to the other planets, Mars and the Earth are relatively similar in the length of their day.

Mars' axis is inclined 25 degrees toward the plane of its orbit around the Sun. This figure is also astonishingly similar to the inclination of the Earth: 23.5 degrees. This tilt means that during its orbit around the Sun the northern and southern hemispheres are alternately further away from or closer to the Sun. Thus Mars has seasonal changes like those on Earth, with considerable temperature variations. Since Mars' orbit is twice as long as the Earth's, however, its seasons are also twice as long. In addition, the effects of the seasons are considerably intensified or softened by the varying distance from the Sun. Since Mars is so much further from the Sun than Earth is, it is generally much, much colder there than here.

Human beings studied the starry heavens long before the invention of the telescope. We now know that humans were already aware of five of the Sun's nine "wandering stars" (the Greek word *planetes* means "wanderer") in prehistoric times. In addition to Mars they knew Mercury, Venus, Jupiter, and Saturn. The earliest known writings concerning Mars are found on Assyrian clay tablets from about 650 BC. According to these records the Red Planet was already associated with a god of war at least 4,000 years ago.

When did humans first notice Mars?

For early humans these mysterious heavenly lights traveling along their irregular paths were something very different than planets and stars are for us today. They saw these wandering stars as unknown forces that influenced life on Earth. The reddish Mars played a particularly important role for many cultures. They gave this "star" imaginative names and associated magical powers with its appearance and disappearance. Whenever it appeared its conspicuous red color suggested blood and fire or war and destruction.

To see how strongly the views of early humans still influence our sense of the universe, we only need to look at our calendar. The number of "wandering stars" known at that time (five planets and two they thought were planets, the Sun and Moon) became a magic number with divine powers. The enormous importance of the number seven shows up in the number of days in the week. The weekday Tuesday was sacred to Mars. From the Latin *martes dies* (day of Mars) we get the French *mardi*, Italian *martedí*, and Spanish *martes* (all of which mean "Tuesday").

More and more these early people began to see living, divine beings in the planets. The color of Mars suggested it brought destruction and thus it became the god of war himself. The Greeks in particular saw in Mars their war god Ares, a god who scorned laws and was a conniving villain. This was how Homer described him in his epics of the gods. Among the Romans Ares became the much revered and worshiped god Mars. His sons Romulus and Remus were believed to be the founders of Rome. Germanic tribes in Northern Europe also had their gods and their name for Mars was Tiu (from which we get Tuesday).

In the 13th century some scholars began studying the positions of the planets, hoping they would help them find the "philosopher's stone," which they believed could turn lead into gold and give eternal life. These mythological and astrological roots of the study of stars and planets came to an end with the beginning of the modern age. A series of discoveries and inventions, together with the theories of great thinkers, created the necessary foundation for the development of modern astronomical research methods.

This portrait of Tycho Brahe was made during his lifetime.

TYCHO BRAHE is considered the best observer of the skies in a time when there weren't any telescopes. He was also a very eccentric person. He had a golden tip made for his nose to replace the "original" that he had lost in a duel as a young man.

Unlike Kepler, who analyzed Brahe's data and came to new theoretical insights, Tycho Brahe still believed the Sun orbited around the Earth.

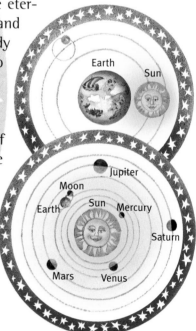

According to the old geocentric model of the world, all of the celestial bodies revolve around the Earth. The heliocentric model places the Sun in the center.

KEPLER was Tycho Brahe's last assistant and after Brahe's death he developed three famous laws that even today are still used when scientists calculate planetary orbits. One of these laws states that planets move along elliptical paths that have the Sun as one of their foci. In 1605 he reached the important conclusion that Mars' orbit is not a circle but rather an ellipse.

Johannes Kepler, 17th century astronomer and mathematician.

GIOVANNI D. CASSINI was professor of astronomy in Bologna from 1650 to 1669, and then went to Paris and became the first director of the observatory there. His work led to many important insights. Among other things, he was the first to calculate accurately the distance from the Earth to the Sun.

When were the first precise observations of Mars made?

For humans to free themselves from the magical world of the gods, they had to learn that celestial bodies are physical objects. When the telescope was invented in the early 17th century, it became impossible to ignore this fact. Now astronomers could see actual planetary spheres that stood out as clearly defined disks next to the stars, which still remained shimmering points of light.

The last great stargazer who worked without a telescope was the Danish astronomer Tycho Brahe (1546–1601). Over a 20-year period, using simple devices that measured angles and time, he prepared very exact planetary tables—especially of Mars. On the basis of this work one of his assistants, Johannes Kepler (1571-1630), later formulated laws governing planetary orbits. Kepler was a theoretician, and the only "tools" he used were the figures Brahe left him.

In 1610 Galileo Galilei (1564–1642) became the first human being to look through a telescope.

During his observations of Mars he still wasn't able to make out any details. The first drawing of Mars that showed any surface features was drawn by a Dutch scholar, Christian Huygens (1629-1695). It is a simple freehand sketch. In a book he published in 1689, Huygens speculated on the possibility of inhabitants on other planets. Because of similarities between Earth and Mars, he depicts Mars as a world related to our Earth, as a kind of "brother of the Earth." Another pioneer of early telescope observation was the Italian scholar Giovanni Cassini (1625–1712). His sketches of Mars already show the white polar caps of Mars. He calculated the length of Mars' day as 24 hours and 40 minutes, only 2.5 minutes longer than the presently accepted value. As the telescope improved, the first maps of Mars were prepared. The astronomer Giovanni Schiaparelli (1835–1910) produced the first usable map.

The year 1877 was to become the great "Mars year." Scientists discovered the two moons of Mars, and the famous "Mars canals" were also mentioned for the first time.

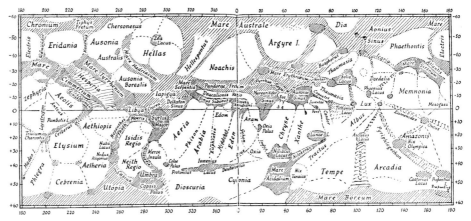

This detailed map of Mars is the work of several astronomers. They produced it from telescope observations they made during the oppositions of 1939 and 1941 and from high-resolution photographs. The map also gives the Latin names for most of the landmarks we can see from Earth.

By 1878 the general public had also become interested in Mars research. The catalyst for this interest was a report by Giovanni Schiaparelli on the canals on Mars. These "canals" were long, fine lines—barely visible—against a light background between darker zones. The press immediately picked up the misleading formulation "Martian canals" and combined it with bold speculations about living beings on Mars. This report unleashed a wave of excitement about Mars. It wasn't just ordinary people who jumped to the conclusion that life on Mars had been proven—even some scientists did so as well. Water was scarce on Mars, they reasoned, and these Martians were forced to bring it to their cities via huge canal systems. Reputable astronomers wrote serious articles about civilization on Mars and claimed that it was much more advanced than our own. They described Mars' scientific and technological accomplishments in great detail.

At the end of the 19th century there were a few astronomers who confirmed Schiaparelli's claim that there was a network of thin, dark lines on the surface of Mars. Even then, however, there were experts who never saw any such "canal" on Mars, despite their larger telescopes. Today we know that many

> **Why was the discovery of the canals on Mars so spectacular?**

of these astronomers were fooled by an optical illusion. When faced with a large number of unclear details at a great distance, the human eye tends to connect such details by means of imaginary auxiliary lines.

Schiaparelli himself gave a very cautious assessment of his own conclusions—he recognized that the object of his studies was at the limits of what was observable in his day. The suggestion that the lines on the Red Planet were artificial waterways did not come from him. This bold suggestion stems from other astronomers and lay persons. The press as a mass medium did the rest.

It is amazing that the idea of canals on Mars was seriously discussed for about 90 years. As late as 1949 a respected journalist claimed that the canals really exist. Photographs from the Mariner 9 space probe finally disproved the "canal theories" and related ideas about intelligent life on Mars.

A PRIZE offered by the French Academy of Science in 1900 shows just how seriously people took suggestions that there might be intelligent life on Mars. The academy offered a prize to the first person who could establish contact with an extraterrestrial being. The description of the contest specifically mentioned Mars.

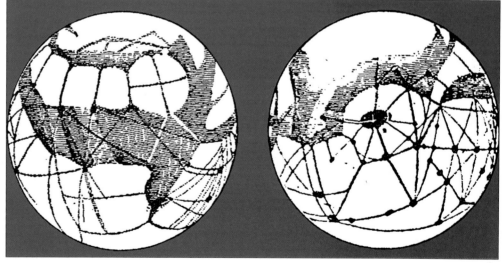

These drawings of Mars were made in 1895 by Percival Lowell (1855–1916). He played a central role in the stir caused by the supposed discovery of canals on Mars. He came from a rich family and was originally a diplomat. In 1894 he founded his own observatory and in the following years published three books as a private scholar and researcher. In these books he argued that there were living beings on Mars that looked different than humans but were just as intelligent.

What do present-day telescopes show on Mars?

For astronomers in the past as well as in the present Mars is small when seen from the Earth and difficult to observe—even if you are looking through a telescope. Over the course of centuries, however, more and more powerful telescopes have brought Mars considerably closer to us. It is best viewed when the Earth—on the "inside track"—passes the more slowly orbiting Mars once every 26 months. In the best of cases it is then only 35 million miles away from us. With one of the huge, modern telescopes it then appears as a small yellowish red disk. So far, observations with larger telescopes have shown several dark spots on Mars and, with particular clarity, the two bright polar caps. Most of the time Mars is much further away from us and thus not as easy to study.

The Hubble Telescope (1990) has opened up new possibilities for observation of Mars. Since it orbits the Earth outside of its disruptive atmosphere it is able to take much clearer pictures of other planets than a telescope on the Earth can. With its 7.5-foot mirror this orbiting observatory sends back such clear pictures of Mars that you can recognize objects no more than 30 miles across. With the Hubble Telescope we can now constantly monitor the changes of seasons, the fluctuating size of the polar caps, and dust storms on the Red Planet.

The Hubble Telescope, photographed from the Space Shuttle Discovery. In this photo the telescope is still attached to the manipulator system of the space shuttle. The solar panels and antennas haven't been unfolded yet.

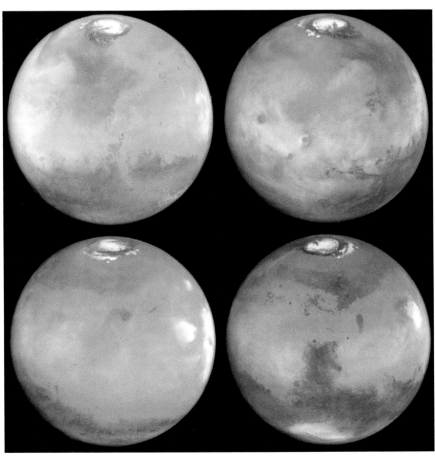

Hubble's photos of Mars—from 62 million miles away—show numerous details on the surface of the Red Planet. In each succeeding image Mars has revolved 90° further. What the pictures show is the transition from spring to summer in the northern hemisphere of the planet. Scientists used such pictures to plan future missions.

The photo in the upper left clearly shows the icy cap on the northern pole, surrounded by a dark ring of sand dunes. The part of the planet in the center of this picture is where Pathfinder landed on July 4th, 1997.

In the picture in the upper right you can easily see the Tharsis volcanoes. They are veiled by a thin layer of clouds.

The picture in the lower left shows a region that seems to have very few features that stand out.

The picture on the lower right shows the darkest formation on Mars' surface, the Syrtis Major. Near the southern pole lies Hellas, a gigantic crater with a diameter of about 1,200 miles. In winter it is covered with dry ice and hidden by clouds.

Why do people believe in intelligent life on Mars?

It wasn't only in the 19th century that people liked to talk about the "little green men" that supposedly live on Mars. Even today the notion that there might be life on Mars continues to attract great attention. We even find a modern form of Mars hysteria in the first half of the 20th century. In 1938 a radio station broadcast a radio play entitled "The War of the Worlds." It was based on a futuristic novel by the British novelist H.G. Wells and depicted the invasion of the Earth by hostile Martians. Well-known director Orson Welles broadcast the radio play as a radio news report. His production was so frighteningly realistic that thousands of people left their homes during the broadcast and fled to the countryside. A few desperate listeners even committed suicide.

The intense interest of scientists and of the general population for the planet Mars has in no way lessened since then. Today the interest expresses itself in scientific space probe programs that serve to gather more and more detailed information about the Red Planet. The search for life also plays an important role in these expeditions.

The pictures sent back by the Viking probe were a new occasion for speculation, since some of the pictures showed objects that appeared to be man-made structures. In particular there is a mountain that seems to have the form of a human face. There are also the so-called pyramids, formations that look like their Egyptian namesakes under certain lighting conditions. Under these circumstances it isn't surprising that bold fantasies about intelligent life on Mars are sprouting up once again. These "structures" are supposed to be the remains of an extinct civilization.

The discovery of tiny structures in a piece of Mars that landed on the Earth—a meteorite—has also fired new discussions among scientists. It is possible, namely, that these structures were formed by bacteria-like organisms about 3.6 billion years ago. Other researchers believe the structures could have been formed in a purely inorganic manner, that is, without the presence of any living organisms. New space probes that are able to analyze the

The broadcast of "The War of the Worlds" on the 30th of October, 1938, is now famous because of the many listeners who believed what Orson Welles so convincingly recited: "I'm speaking to you from the roof of broadcast building in New York. The bells you hear are ringing to warn the people to evacuate the city as the Martians approach. It's estimated that three million people have moved out along the road to the north."

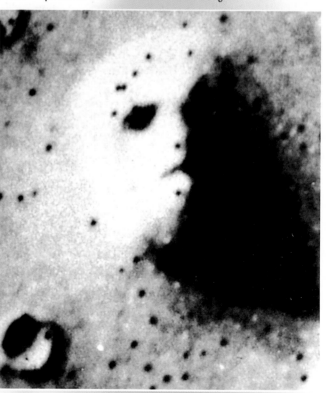

The "Face of Mars."

Without the many science fiction novels and films about Mars, modern Mars research might not have developed as quickly as it has. Many famous researchers have described how these works fired their imagination when they were young. Science fiction author Ray Bradbury may have been right when, in 1974, he accused a science fiction writer who always set his stories on Mars of sending ten-year-olds the message that they should run out into the yard, stretch out their arms, and fly to Mars.

surface of the planet may tell us more clearly whether or not there has ever been life on Mars. It may be, however, that this question won't be definitely answered until astronauts land on Mars at some point in the future.

The best methods for recording the surface features of a planet or moon are either to draw or to photograph the surfaces in question. Researchers can then locate landmarks and determine distances between them. A map like this is

What did it take to get modern research started?

in the United States evaluated all available maps and photographs of the planet and located all clearly recognizable details on a coordinate grid. By laying this imaginary network of orientation points over the surface, these scientists were able to determine the positions of the most important surface features to within 30 miles—instead of 300 miles, as had previously been the case.

With these geographical reference points and an exact measurement of the time it takes Mars to orbit the Sun, astronomers could now predict which side of the planet would be facing the Sun at a given time, and at what angle.

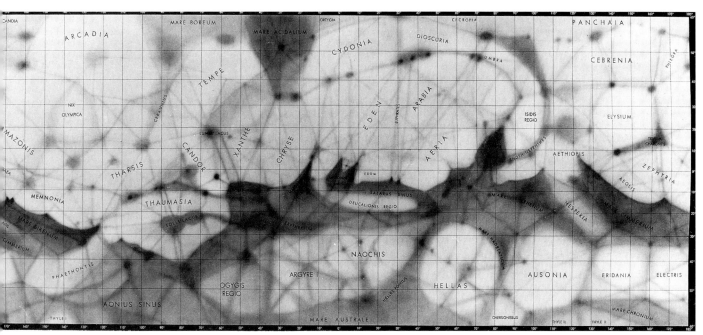

This is certainly one of the best maps based on telescopic observations from Earth. Many astronomers worked on this map. In addition to the polar zones it also shows the most important and most striking light and dark formations and their Latin names. This map was the basis for much of the planning for the first American Mars probe.

indispensable for scientists who have to calculate a space probe's course and program the orientation of its instruments to focus on specific points on the surface.

Before the first Mars probes were launched, planetary scientists

This was necessary for the planning of the space probe missions. Planners had to decide in advance which side of the planet the probe would fly past, so that they could set the cameras to photograph specific surface features.

Our Understanding of Mars Today

MARS—THE FOCUS OF RESEARCH IN OUR SOLAR SYSTEM

Areas of Concentration in Mars Research:

- atmosphere
- water and ice
- plate tectonics
- volcanic activity
- sedimentation
- erosion
- morphology
- impact phenomena
- stratigraphy (determining the age of rock layers)
- topography
- chemical-mineralogical composition
- physical character of the surface

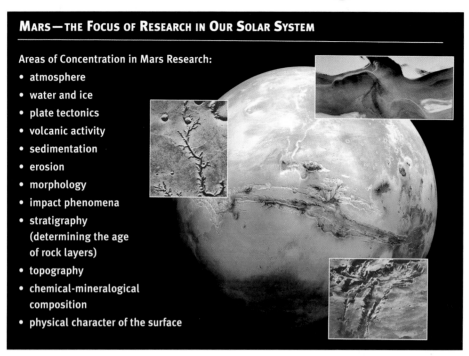

Data on the **MAGNETIC FIELD** of Mars has made it clear to scientists that the matter in the interior of the planet is very unevenly distributed. The only thing we know for sure is that the core consists of metals and very heavy types of rock. The upper layers are made of lighter rock. In the course of their research scientists also discovered that Mars deviates slightly from a perfect spherical form. It has several indentations and protrusions, but they measure only a few hundred feet and are not visible to telescopes.

What is the structure of the planet's interior?

It isn't easy to analyze the interior of a planet. Even on Earth our huge drilling machines can only reach down to depths of 6 or 7 miles—barely scratching the surface. Geologists are thus forced to rely on indirect methods of measuring when they investigate the inner structure of a planet. One method is to measure seismic waves—the waves created by movements in the Earth. Since these waves travel at different rates through different materials, scientists can use them to determine the inner structure of the planet. Measuring stations around the world record the waves from earthquakes. Changes in the waves as they pass through the globe give scientists an indication of the different levels of rock or mineral in the center of the Earth.

Investigations like this are of course much more difficult on other planets since the landing capsule is the only measuring station available. Quakes on the surface of Mars are also rare, since its center has cooled so much. Scientists therefore use a different method in their investigations of Mars. The magnetic field that surrounds a planet is generated by the mass in its interior. Mars probes are steered through the magnetic field of the planet. By comparing the readings from the paths taken by different probes scientists can reach indirect conclusions about the different layers of the planet's core. To do this, however, they need very precise monitoring methods that have only been developed in the last few years.

This model of Mars shows the thick, cooled crust and beneath it the core, with a diameter of about 1,250 miles. The core is still very hot. Slow movements in this sluggishly flowing core generate the weak magnetic field that was recently discovered by Mars Global Surveyor. The lines on this drawing show the magnetic field as it may have been many, many years ago. Today only a weak remainder surrounds the planet, since there is hardly any movement in the core.

What is Mars' surface like?

Even looking through a small amateur telescope, hobby astronomers can see several details on the surface of Mars—if they have at least 100x magnification. First, they will probably recognize one of the bright polar caps. Then, after a few minutes of getting used to the dim image, they may see one or two dark spots on the reddish disk.

The extremes in elevation on the surface of Mars range from about 3.7 miles below mean level in the Hellas Plains (a gigantic crater) to 16.8 miles above mean level at the peak of the giant volcano, Olympus Mons.

Before landers set down on the Red Planet in the mid-seventies, experts had only very vague ideas about the composition of the soil on Mars—its reddish color points to a high iron oxide content.

The two Viking probes landed in a region that lies about 1.25 miles below mean level. The atmospheric pressure is minimally higher there and scientists hoped this would give them a greater chance of finding evidence that there was once water on the planet, and perhaps even evidence of simple life forms.

The landers' two x-ray spectrometers made it possible to analyze the chemical-physical structure of Mars' soil for the first time (see table).

Analysis of Mars' Soil at the Viking 1 Landing Site

oxygen	40%
silicon	18.5–24.5 %
iron	12.5–14.5 %
potassium	8 %
calcium	3–5.5 %
magnesium	2.5–5.5 %
sulfur	2.5–5 %
aluminum	2–5 %
cesium	0.1–0.6 %

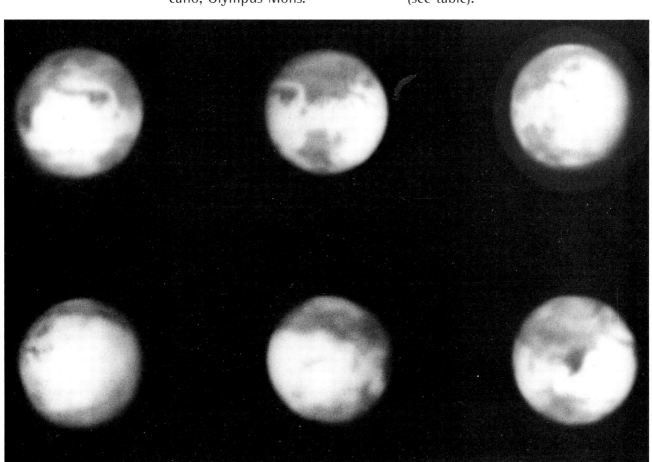

These six black-and-white photographs show the daily rotation of Mars. They were taken in 1969 by the 5-foot telescope of the Cataline Observatory while Mars was at a point in its orbit where it is particularly close to Earth. By using a red filter on the camera, researchers were able to make details more visible than usual. The smallest recognizable details are probably 30 miles across.

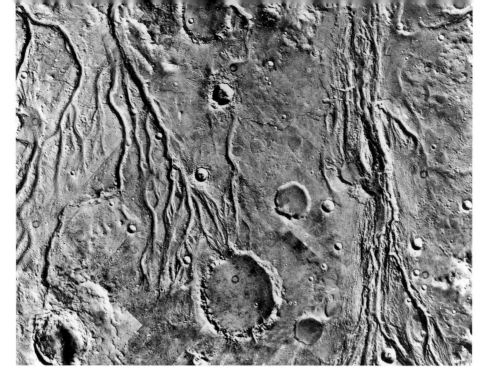

The details of the surface of Mars are extremely varied, as you can see from this picture. It looks like many large river valleys run through the landscape. This photo-mosaic was pieced together from pictures taken by the Viking 1 orbiter over the region called Chryse Planitia. On this sloping terrain you can clearly see the paths rivers carved on their way down through mountain ranges and craters. After all, the change in elevation from high point to low point here is almost 2 miles. The picture gives the impression that some of the craters were formed after the large water masses dried up. Many of the rivers seem to have arisen in older craters. Sometimes they also end in craters. Breaks in the crater walls are clearly visible.

Were there once rivers on Mars?

It created quite a stir in scientific circles when, in 1972, the space probe Mariner 9 discovered riverbeds in several places on the surface of Mars. Of course there isn't any water in them anymore, but the shape of these surface features suggests that billions of years ago there may have been broad, raging torrents and narrow, winding rivers on Mars. These riverbeds always occur where the land drops off, and downstream they often branch out and form deltas that then disappear into the Martian landscape.

Rivers on the Earth usually form from melting snow high in the mountains, but on Mars it was probably groundwater, rising to the surface in irregular intervals, that gave rise to rivers that then poured out into the plains. One theory holds that it was once much, much warmer on the planet and that huge ice masses melted into the ground on Mars.

If, in the past, masses of water flowed across the surface of Mars for millions of years, then it is possible that simple living organisms developed. This hope has motivated many scientists to look for evidence of such life. Experts also speculate on the causes of the warming on Mars so long ago. The change in climate was probably caused by a change in the orientation of Mars' rotational axis. Furthermore, according to another assumption of many experts, the atmosphere must have been much denser billions of years ago, since water rising to the surface of the planet would otherwise have evaporated very quickly.

Scientists don't know for sure if there is still water on Mars, and if so, how much. If there is water, however, then it is held frozen in the sandy-rocky surface of the planet. It isn't unthinkable that Mars' rotational axis might again shift over several more millions of years, and that temperatures might then rise again and melt the water held frozen in the surface.

WATER ON MARS

In February of 1998, NASA published pictures taken by Mars Global Surveyor. They clearly show a dry riverbed. This is the first real evidence that there was water on Mars billions of years ago. Until this point scientists couldn't really be sure.

What gave rise to the volcanoes and craters on Mars?

Like all other bodies in our solar system, billions of years ago Mars was bombarded by meteorites of all sizes from outer space. They created thousands of craters on its surface. Naturally, over the course of millions of years atmospheric conditions and the strong winds on Mars have leveled out many of these crater rings and left only parts of them visible. This explains why there are far fewer craters on Mars in comparison to the Earth's moon or the planet Mercury. Neither of these bodies has an atmosphere and the only "weathering" that occurs there is caused by the extreme temperature swings from day to night. Nearly all the impact craters that once marked the Earth's surface have disappeared as a result of various geological changes and weathering processes.

A typical kind of crater on Mars is the so-called mud crater, which is surrounded by deposits of crumbly material ejected from the crater. This material might be cooled lava from the depths of the planet, or it might be the remains of melted surface rock. It is probably just the remains from the melting of frozen soil that was heated by a meteorite collision and then solidified again.

Scientists were also surprised when they examined the pictures taken by Mariner 9 and discovered a few gigantic volcanoes on Mars. Observers on Earth had already seen the huge volcanic cones on the Tharsis Plateau, but hadn't recognized their true nature. These shield volcanoes are around 250 million years old and have long been extinct. Since Mars' gravity is much weaker than Earth's they grew extremely high and didn't sink into the surface as much as volcanoes on Earth do. The largest volcano on Mars is Olympus Mons. It is 16.8 miles high and its base has a diameter of nearly 375 miles. The edge of the crater is sharply defined, but the slopes are smooth. An observer standing at the foot of this volcano would have a hard time making out the peak some 180 miles away. Since Mars is smaller than Earth, its surface is also more curved than Earth's, and this, too, would limit visibility. The closest parallel on Earth is Mauna Loa volcano on the Island of Hawaii, which has a base diameter of about 125 miles and is more than 5.5 miles high. All we see, however, is the top half that rises above the ocean surface (see illustration on page 16).

This colored photo-mosaic from pictures taken by the Viking 1 orbiter shows the peak of 16.8-mile-high Olympus Mons by morning light. The crater area has a diameter of about 50 miles and consists of several ring-shaped terraces. There are few signs of impact craters, so the volcano must be relatively young in geological terms. The high cloud cover and the fields of fog on the slopes of the giant volcano—up to a height of 15 miles—are particularly noteworthy. They consist primarily of ice from water that cooled on the slopes of the volcano. They are so extensive they can sometimes be seen even from Earth. By the afternoon of a Mars day these clouds have burned off.

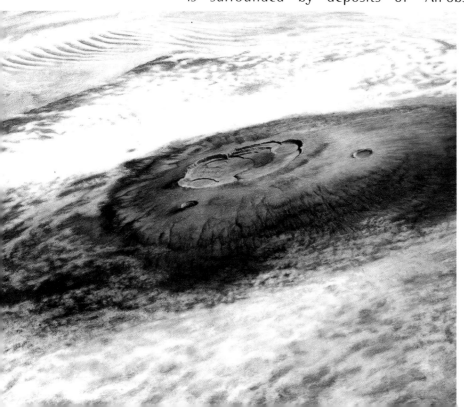

What caused the many gorges and dunes on Mars?

Judging from the photographs taken by space probes, the Red Planet is more deeply furrowed than any other planet in our solar system—except for Earth. The gorges vary greatly in length and breadth. The spectrum extends from short, winding beds of former rivers to the gigantic canyon Valles Marineris. The edges of this enormous rift display an amazing variety. They are broken up by smaller gorges that have eaten their way into the surrounding plateau like fjords. There are also many rifts and gorges on the Tharsis ridge in the area around the four large volcano cones.

Another thing that stands out about the surface of Mars are the numerous large and small dunes—

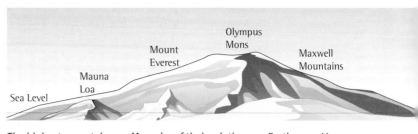

The highest mountains on Mars dwarf their relatives on Earth or on Venus (Maxwell Mountains). Olympus Mons on Mars has a volume more than 20 times that of Mauna Loa in the Hawaiian Islands. The weaker surface gravity on Mars is one of the reasons why mountains there can become so much larger than on Earth.

otherwise found only in desert areas on Earth. The sand masses on the Red Planet are moved across great distances, primarily by the massive storms in Mars' atmosphere. Even in the limited area within some impact craters there are occasionally fields of dunes. The weaker gravity on Mars and the high wind speeds both help explain why the dunes are so much larger than dunes on Earth and why the intervals between ridges are so much greater.

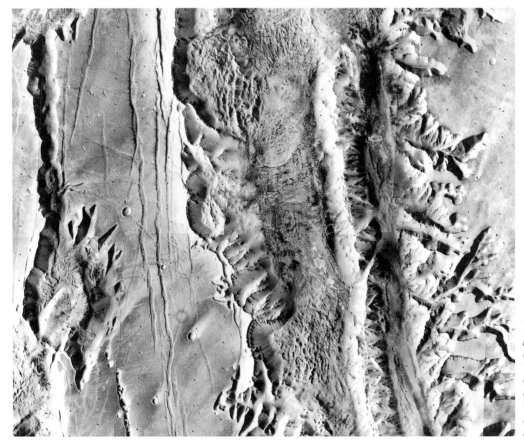

This photo-mosaic was pieced together from many images taken by the Viking 1 orbiter in August of 1976. It shows a section of the gigantic canyon Valles Marineris with its deep gorges and side canyons.

How was Mars' giant canyon formed?

Mariner 9's year-long mission in Mars' orbit in the year 1972 was extremely successful—in part, because it discovered a wealth of curious surface formations on the planet. The most impressive formation from a geological standpoint is without doubt the enormous canyon running along the equator. It has many branches and side canyons and is similar to the Grand Canyon on Earth—except that it is 100 times bigger. This gigantic rift was named "Valles Marineris" as a reminder of the fact that it was the Mariner space probe that first discovered what it was really like.

This large scar on Mars' surface runs through the region that was given the Latin name *Coprates Regio* on maps drawn in an age before space probes. It is possible to see the canyon from the Earth using a telescope, but it was Mariner 9's cameras that first showed its enormous dimensions. It is more than 2,400 miles long and up to 125 miles wide in places. It ranges from .5 to 3.7 miles in depth.

Photographs from Mariner 9 showed the rough outlines of the gigantic canyon, but the cameras on the Viking probe first gave us really sharp images of Valles Marineris. With these photographs geologists were able to start working on an analysis of the canyon's formation.

According to their findings, this rift along the equator of Mars was probably torn open in the planet's crust by massive quakes. A second supposition is that the Mariner Valley formed in much the same way as the Atlantic Basin on Earth, that is, as a result of continental plates drifting apart. The Mid-Atlantic Ridge—the huge, underwater mountain range between Europe and America—also has its counterpart in the Mariner rift. Both have a central bulge of hardened lava.

The giant canyon Valles Marineris on Mars extends nearly 2,500 miles from east to west, as this projection onto an outline of the United States shows. The huge rift's breadth from north to south is 125 miles at its widest point. In some places it reaches a depth of nearly 4 miles.

This photograph shows very clearly why Mars' asteroid moons (asteroid is another name for planetoid) are sometimes called "space potatoes."

When these mini-moons were first discovered, scientists calculated their size indirectly, based on their apparent brightness and the assumption that their surface had average reflective qualities. The Viking photographs taken in the 70's made it possible to measure the moons exactly. According to these figures the larger one, which orbits closer to the planet, is about 11.8 by 14 by 16.8 miles in size, and the smaller moon, which is further from the planet, measures about 6.2 by 7.5 by 9.3 miles.

The distances of the moons from the center of Mars are 5,870 miles for Phobos and 14,290 for Deimos. The duration of their orbits around Mars is 7 hours 39 minutes for Phobos and 30 hours 18 minutes for Deimos. Both moons have orbits roughly following the equator. Since they are so close to the planet, an observer on Mars would only be able to see them from a small band along the equator.

Both moons have irregular shapes. They are also covered with craters of every size and are scored with long furrows. As a result they are sometimes called "space potatoes." Their surfaces are covered with a layer of dark dust that reflects only a small percentage of the Sun's light. Experts agree that these moons are captured asteroids—that is, they are objects from the planetoid belt that lies between Mars and Jupiter. Many millions of years ago they presumably came so close to Mars that they were captured by its gravity and pulled into orbit around it.

The orbit of PHOBOS, the inner moon, is growing smaller and smaller according to astronomers. In 10 to 100 million years it will have come so close that it will crash onto the surface of Mars. This will create a new and gigantic impact crater.

This photograph of Phobos, the larger of Mars' two moons, was taken in August 1998 by Mars Global Surveyor from a distance of 671 miles. It takes in a section of the surface that is about 5 by 7 miles in size. The clearly recognizable furrows in the surface of Phobos are dozens of miles long and from .6 to 1.2 miles wide. The surface of this moon seems to be covered by a layer of dust many feet in thickness.

How did Mars get two moons?

Mars has two very small moons. Since they are so close to the brightly shining planet, they are among our solar system's most difficult objects to observe. To see these minute points of light next to the planet, observers must block out the image of the planet itself. The two mini-moons were discovered in 1877 by American astronomer Asaph Hall with the telescope in the Washington Observatory. Its lens was 3 feet in diameter. This was about the same time that the Italian Schiaparelli first reported his claims about canals on Mars. Since the planet was named after Mars, the god of war, these two moons were named Phobos and Deimos, fear and terror. According to Greek mythology, Phobos and Deimos were the attendants of the war god.

Climate and Weather on Mars

The probability that the temperature at some point on Mars might be 32° F (0° C) at this moment—the melting point for water—is extremely small. Conditions for the **DEVELOPMENT OF SIMPLEST LIFE FORMS** on Mars are thus very unfavorable at present, since liquid water would be required.

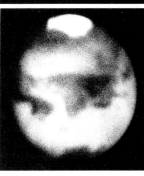

The top photograph was taken with a blue filter. What it shows is primarily the atmosphere surrounding Mars. The diameter of the Mars image in this photo is larger than the diameter of the image in the photo below it. It was taken with a red filter and shows details of Mars' surface. The region around the well-known formation Meridiani Sinus is clearly recognizable.

What is the composition of Mars' atmosphere?

This question is particularly interesting since the composition of the atmosphere is one of the factors that determine whether or not life is possible on a planet. Photography has already provided impressive proof that Mars does indeed have an atmosphere. If we take two photographs of Mars, one with a red filter and one with a blue filter, the pictures show a slight difference in the diameter of the planet's photographic image. The blue-filtered exposure records the atmosphere. Mars appears somewhat larger in this image than in the one produced with a red filter—it basically records the planet's solid body. From this difference scientists conclude that Mars' rather thin atmosphere reaches up to a height of 125 miles (200 km). In the photo taken with a blue filter, you can see bright clouds over the planet's poles—they are formed from ice crystals.

In 1965, Mariner 4 finally gave astronomers more precise information about the composition of Mars' atmosphere. According to its information, the atmosphere is 95% carbon dioxide. From the Viking landers we now know that the other 5% of the gaseous envelope surrounding Mars is made up of helium and the noble gas argon, together with traces of oxygen and water vapor. Since then we also know that the composition of Mars' atmosphere varies depending on the time of the year.

The atmospheric pressure on Mars is very low and varies between 3 and 8 millibars. The air pressure on Earth is about 1000 millibars or 1 bar. Still the atmosphere on Mars displays several amazing parallels to that of Earth. Air pressure drops with rising altitude, 10 percent with each rise of 1 kilometer (6/10 of a mile). Mars also has an ozone layer in its atmosphere, and in summer it disappears over the poles, as Mariner 6 and Mariner 7 discovered.

Because of its elliptical orbit, the distance from Mars to the Sun varies over the course of a Mars year. Temperatures also fluctuate greatly as a result. They range from −202° F (−130° C) to just below 32° F (0° C), as the two Viking landers discovered by recording temperatures over the course of one year. The Viking 1 landing site was approximately mid-way between the north pole and the equator. The lowest temperature it recorded there was −121° F (−85° C) at 5 o'clock in the morning, just before sunrise. The highest value it recorded was −18.4° F (−28° C), at 2 o'clock in the afternoon, Mars time, just after the Sun passed its highest point in the sky. At the poles temperatures sink during the night to −190° F (−123° C) or even lower, as indirect measurements have shown.

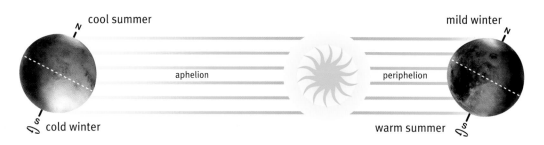

cool summer
mild winter

aphelion
periphelion

cold winter
warm summer

What effects do seasons have on Mars?

Because its rotational axis is tilted 24° toward the plane of its orbit around the Sun, Mars, like the Earth, has very distinct seasons. This tilted orientation leads to large fluctuations in the intensity of solar radiation during the planet's yearly orbit around the Sun. This, in turn, leads to significant swings in temperature.

Just as on Earth, the Mars hemisphere that is currently tilted toward the Sun experiences summer. The days are long and the Sun is high overhead at noon. At the same time the other hemisphere is experiencing winter. There the Sun can only radiate the surface for a short time each day and from a low angle. It is therefore cold there, and ice and frozen carbon dioxide ("dry ice") form at the poles.

On Mars the intensity of the seasons and their duration is weakened or strengthened by the planet's varying distance from the Sun.

The difference in distance to the Sun at its closest and furthest points is 25 million miles (40 million km). The two effects—the tilt of its axis and its distance from the Sun—overlap and either intensify or weaken the temperature fluctuations.

We now know that the climate on Mars has also changed significantly over large spans of time—hundreds of millions of years—in addition to the small-scale seasonal changes. The causes of the change were, on the one hand, major, long-term fluctuations in the tilt of the planet's rotational axis; and on the other hand, great variations in Mars' distance from the Sun during its yearly orbit. In the course of millions of years this would also have caused strong fluctuations in the intensity of solar radiation striking the planet. In some stage of the planet's history it may have become so warm that the permafrost trapped in the planet's soil may have melted and flowed across the surface in gigantic rivers.

When Mars is at the point in its orbit that is furthest from the Sun (aphelion) it is summer in the northern hemisphere and winter in the southern hemisphere. Because of the great distance the summer is cool and the winter is very cold. When Mars passes through the orbital point nearest the Sun (perihelion), there is a mild winter in the northern hemisphere and a relatively hot summer in the southern one.

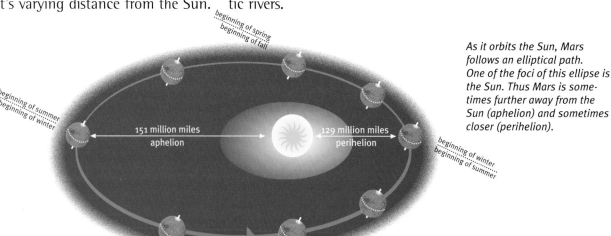

beginning of spring
beginning of fall

beginning of summer
beginning of winter

151 million miles
aphelion

129 million miles
perihelion

beginning of winter
beginning of summer

beginning of fall
beginning of spring

As it orbits the Sun, Mars follows an elliptical path. One of the foci of this ellipse is the Sun. Thus Mars is sometimes further away from the Sun (aphelion) and sometimes closer (perihelion).

The cameras of the Viking probes gave us a completely new image of Mars' northern polar zone. It is covered by many thin layers of frozen carbon dioxide (dry ice). This black-and-white picture shows an area about 225 miles wide. You can see many fissures and faults and also glacier-like formations in the sheet of dry ice.

Why do the polar caps interest scientists so much?

Even the earliest observers of Mars came to the conclusion that the bright polar caps they saw through their telescopes might be ice deposits. Finally in 1951 the Dutch-American planetary researcher Gerard Kuiper (1905-1973) succeeded in proving that there was indeed ice at the northern and southern poles of Mars.

Several years later a French astronomer, Gerard de Vaucouleurs, recognized that the dark edges of the polar caps were wet regions. He also showed that the bright poles really do grow smaller in the summer since some of the water evaporates. This cloud of water vapor 6 to 12 miles above the poles of Mars can be detected even from Earth. In winter the water vapor freezes and falls to the surface. The polar caps expand again.

As they flew past Mars in 1969, the Mariner 6 and Mariner 7 space probes sent back pictures confirming that the southern pole is one of the most interesting geological regions on the planet. From the deeply furrowed landscape researchers are able to gain numerous insights into the processes that led to the formation of the present surface of Mars.

Detailed analysis of the Viking pictures of the two poles also showed that the rotational axis of the planet and its distance from the Sun must have fluctuated dramatically over the course of billions of years. When the northern ice cap shrinks during the Mars summer, we can see numerous deep rifts such as were formed on Earth during our ice ages. The band of dark sand and stone surrounding the polar ice caps is also noteworthy. This region is apparently damp from time to time, and earlier observers of the planet believed they had discerned traces of vegetation. There has been no sign of vegetation in any of the space probe photographs, however.

Mars' northern polar region, photographed by Mars Global Surveyor in September 1998.

What changes do we see in Mars' poles?

Mars' elliptical orbit—and the resulting fluctuations in distance from the Sun—has a pronounced effect on its seasons. It influences temperatures on the surface and also the size of the polar caps in summer and winter.

In the southern hemisphere of Mars the polar cap recedes so

dioxide in the atmosphere to fall to the surface as bright CO_2 snow. This cap reaches much greater dimensions than the water ice caps. In the case of the northern pole, its ice cap sometimes reaches down as far as the 40th degree of latitude. On Earth this would mean that the ice reached all the way down to New York City.

Scientists are unable to agree whether or not there are large

These three photographs show how the ice cap on the north pole of Mars grows smaller over the course of a fourth of a Mars year. Using computer technology researchers were able to produce these polar projections

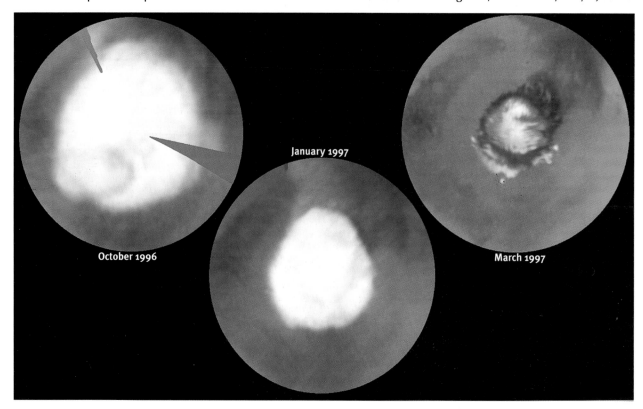

October 1996

January 1997

March 1997

much during the short summer that the majority of the polar landscape becomes visible. The northern polar cap never melts away this much since summer there occurs during "aphelion"—the period when Mars is furthest from the Sun. This cap apparently consists almost entirely of frozen water.

The winters at both poles are still cold enough to cause carbon

quantities of water at the poles. At the south pole alone some researchers estimate there is a water supply of about 120,000 cubic miles. This alone, in a melted state, could form an ocean on Mars 435 miles by 435 miles and more than a half a mile deep, as U.S. researchers have concluded from images sent back by Mariner 9 and Viking 1 and 2.

from several photographs of the planet taken by the Hubble Telescope. Over the course of six Earth months the layer of carbon dioxide snow melts completely in the northern Mars spring, leaving only the small cap of frozen water behind. The dark ring of damp sand dunes is clearly visible around the actual pole. The resolution in these images is approximately 60 miles.

The Mars photos from Mariner 6 and 7 provided unmistakable indications of atmospheric effects in the thin gaseous envelope around Mars. They even showed signs of a kind of weather event. TV images broadcast at that time showed clouds, coatings of hoarfrost, frozen water, and carbon dioxide. Phenomena of this sort showed up frequently on the walls of craters and on high volcanoes or other mountain slopes. The picture here is a wide-angle photograph taken by Mariner 6 from a distance of 3,000 miles. It shows an area roughly 680 by 930 miles. You can see an irregular cloud formation in the upper left.

What types of clouds are there on Mars?

One of the big surprises in the Viking photos were images of different cloud types. Even in the Red Planet's thin atmosphere there are weather phenomena that form as they do on Earth—from humidity (water vapor).

The veil of morning mists spreads over a wide area in the plains on Mars. It forms shortly after sunrise when the Sun's rays evaporate the thin layer of ice on the ground. As it rises higher, the water rapidly condenses again and forms a huge veil of clouds.

Another type of cloud in Mars' atmosphere is the so-called convection cloud. These clouds form when surface gases warm up during the day and rise into the upper atmosphere where they cool and form thin veils of vapor. Clouds of this type are found mostly over plateaus or on the slopes of the big volcanoes. Especially in the northern hemisphere's summer, such bright veils cover large areas of the Red Planet. Sometimes you can even see them from Earth using a large telescope.

The Mariner 9 space probe also discovered wave clouds in the atmosphere on Mars. They form when strong winds sweep across the landscape and run up against a volcanic cone or crater rim. On the side away from the wind, behind the obstacle, wave-shaped clouds form. You can see phenomena like this on Earth when a wide band of clouds over the ocean suddenly hits a tall island and is split.

On Mars these clouds are formed from dry ice. A sharper outline distinguishes them from clouds made of water vapor.

This impressive photo shows a large field of water-ice clouds. They were photographed by the Viking 1 probe shortly after sunrise in the valleys of the canyon region Noctis Labyrinthus ("labyrinth of the night"), near the equator of Mars. The color photograph was formed from three exposures, one each with a blue, green, and red filter.
The area encompassed by the photo is about 60 miles by 60 miles in size. The clouds of bright water vapor stand out clearly against the rust-red background of Mars' soil.

The temperature fluctuations

that occur over the course of a Mars year—and even during the space of a single day—cause violent turbulence in the planet's thin atmosphere. This turbulence regularly gives rise to both localized and very extensive dust storms. They can even become so large that they cloak the entire planet and prevent observers from seeing any surface details.

A global dust storm of this sort raged on the planet around the New Year 1971-1972 as Mariner 9 approached the planet. As a result its instruments and cameras weren't able to "see" anything for several weeks. This sandstorm may also have been the doom of two Soviet Mars probes and their landing capsules. When the two probes reached Mars the Soviets lost contact with them and they failed to transmit any data.

When Mars comes close to the Sun (summer in the southern hemisphere) the formation of such dust storms is particularly noticeable. The radiant heat from the Sun is as much as 45% stronger than usual and leads to violent winds in Mars' atmosphere. Sometimes these winds reach speeds of 250-300 mph, speeds no weather phenomenon on Earth can match, not even a hurricane. The highest wind speeds ever measured on Earth reached a maximum of around 125 mph.

These regular sandstorms are a driving force in erosion on Mars—the gradual weathering and leveling of its surface. Within a short time huge quantities of sand are blown across the Martian landscape at high speeds and "sand down" the surface as it were. In places where we find dunes, these storms may heap up new hills.

A vivid example of erosion on Mars is the Valles Marineris. The older layers have already been weathered away, and sandstorms may well have played an important role in the process. Harder places in Mars' surface crust withstood this wind erosion and now tower up over their surroundings. The side turned away from the wind shows droplet-shaped sand deposits.

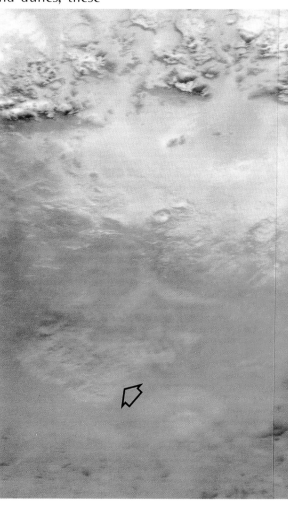

Dust storms on Mars often last for many weeks and darken the atmosphere. This, of course, has an effect on the climate. These storms particularly influence the increase or decrease in the size of the polar ice caps, which in turn changes the water-vapor content of the atmosphere and thus the consistency of the sand. If the sand is wet and heavy, it can't be whirled into the air by wind as easily as dry, loose sand can. Thus the climate on Mars is determined by many different factors that are constantly influencing each other.

The cameras of the Viking 2 orbiter were able to observe the rise of a dust storm in the thin atmosphere of Mars. The eye of the storm shown here is located over the large Argyre impact crater in the southern hemisphere and has a diameter of about 180 miles. Sandstorms in the atmosphere hinder scientists since they obscure the cameras' view of the planet. On the other hand, witnessing the beginning, the development, and the end of a gigantic sandstorm on Mars is also exciting in its own right.

The First American Mars Probes

How have space probes brought us closer to Mars?

For thousands of years astronomers have been bound to the Earth, and it has only been a few centuries that they have had telescopes to reduce the great distance to the planets. With the advent of space probes astronomers suddenly had a revolutionary new tool. Modern rocketry and satellite technology have made an entirely new method of research possible. With the help of space probes, scientists could now bring telescopes and other instruments up close to the planets—from Mercury to Mars and on out to Neptune. Thus much more precise observations and investigations of very, very distant planets have now become possible. The space probes developed by the United States and the Soviet Union/Russia have

finally made it possible for us to discern the actual appearance of the planets and their surfaces, the composition of their atmospheres and rings, and the existence of moons orbiting them. Soon after the launch of the first satellites orbiting Earth in 1957-1958, the space agencies of both superpowers began developing their first planetary space probes.

In the 60's we saw the development of an intense competition between the United States and the Soviet Union, and this competition led to mixed results. The Americans with their space probes were particularly successful in exploring Mars. Soviet researchers had better luck with their study of Venus, which orbits the Sun inside the Earth's orbit.

The strategy of exploring the planets by means of space probes became more and more "directed" over time. At first the probes simply flew past their targets and had a very brief period in which to take measurements. Then orbiters were launched. They entered into a satellite orbit around the planets and could thus carry out investigation over a longer period of time. A further giant step was taken when American and Soviet space agencies launched space probes to Mars and Venus that were equipped with landing capsules. These landing capsules

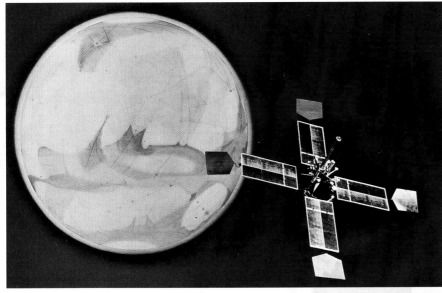

Before the first American space probes were sent to Mars, NASA published several artists' views of the planned mission. They were meant to introduce the public to the stages and goals of the mission. This illustration shows the space probe Mariner 4, with its four characteristic solar panels, approaching the Red Planet. On the artist's depiction of the planet you can see some of the surface formations as they are seen from the Earth with large telescopes.

This special new camera delivered sharp images of the entire surface of Mars and of its two moons from the two Viking orbiters. The lenses both had a focal length of a little more than 1 1/2 feet. The images were recorded on an electronic registering surface and had a resolution of 1,056 lines with 1,182 pixels per line. The image data was then transmitted to Earth. The camera had a filter wheel that allowed different filters to be inserted so that photographs could be made that registered only certain wavelengths of light. From a distance of about 950 miles the cameras took pictures of segments of the surface. The segments measured about 50 miles by 50 miles and showed images as small as 130 feet in diameter.

THE JET PROPULSION LABORATORY builds NASA's Mars probes. This special research center is located in Pasadena, California. For several decades now experts in planetary research have gathered there to develop new projects and to build the necessary space probes. Researchers there also oversee the flight of their probes—which may last several years—and monitor its operation once it reaches its remote destination.

dropped into the planet's atmosphere and landed on the surface.

Now it was possible to do more than map the surface features of the planet. The lander was capable of analyzing soil samples. This advance in space technology also had negative side effects, however. The better equipped the planetary probes were, the heavier they became. The Viking probes are a good example of this problem.

The weight of each of the Viking space probes was the equivalent of two large Mercedes limousines—3.4 tons. This double mission cost around 2 billion dollars. In times of drastic budget cuts for American, Russian, and European space agencies, mammoth projects like this no longer have a chance. Since the end of the 80's, NASA has therefore taken a new approach: faster, cheaper, better. This motto still guides space probe exploration of Mars today. Major advances in lightweight building technology and in shrinking the size of electronic components, cameras, and other scientific instruments make it possible to live

up to the motto. After several years' interruption following the Viking program, NASA now plans

to launch two small, inexpensive spacecraft at each "launch window"—every two years.

The first two probes of the new series have already been employed and were very successful. Mars Pathfinder, which was launched toward the end of 1996 and arrived in the summer of 1997—together with its small Rover Sojourner—and the simultaneous Mars Global Surveyor both achieved their goals and demonstrated the new possibilities of NASA's smaller, more efficient probes.

The relatively small Sojourner is at present one of the most advanced devices that planetary researchers have at their disposal.

A special technological challenge when **BUILDING A SPACE PROBE** lies in the long duration of the missions. The probe contains a mini-laboratory, and it must be kept in good working order during the long flight in the coldness of outer space, so that it can be activated once it reaches its goal. Its work phase on the planet may last as long as the flight itself.

THE TEMPERATURE REGULATION SYSTEM assures that the extreme cold in space—temperatures as low as −148° F (-100° C) or more—doesn't damage sensitive instruments. The Viking probes were in operation for four years. On Pathfinder the instruments only survived for three months.

How does a space probe work?

In the early 60's the United States and the Soviet Union built the first electronic observers for Venus and Mars. They were inspired by their success with Moon probes. A probe of this type not only has to transport scientific instruments, but must also see to it that the instruments remain operational for a period of many months and that they are put into use at the proper times.

The core of a space probe is the base or frame. This contains all necessary operational systems and electronic instrumentation. This includes the on-board computer with its timing mechanism that controls all orbital, positional, and measuring maneuvers, and the communications system for sending and receiving information. The base also contains a data storage device and temperature regulation system. This system keeps the sensitive instruments in the base from getting too hot or too cold.

All of the Mars probes launched so far have been equipped with solar cells mounted on large, collapsible panels. These solar panels supply the probe with energy. They transform light rays into electric energy that is then used to power the probe's systems and the scientific instruments when they are put into use on the distant planet. These panels produce only a few hundred watts of electricity, however—in other words only enough to power the light bulbs in a small apartment. The systems and instruments of a space probe have to function on very little electricity. Much of the available power is used simply to keep especially sensitive instruments warm.

In order to maintain radio contact with Earth, all space probes are outfitted with powerful radio senders and antennas. The dish-shape of the antennas bundles the radio waves so they are easier to pick up on Earth. The larger the antenna, the more information per time unit it can transmit—if there is enough energy available.

In planning a flight past a planet, many factors must be taken into consideration so that the probe can collect the maximum amount of information concerning the distant world. The probe's rapidly changing orientation relative to the planet and its momentary position relative to the Sun and Earth are factors to be considered when implementing an instrument. TV cameras are dependent on good lighting. Other instruments can operate, at least partially, on the night side of the planet. Planners must also take into account the shadowing of the Earth by the destination planet, since during this "eclipse" no radio signals can be transmitted or received.

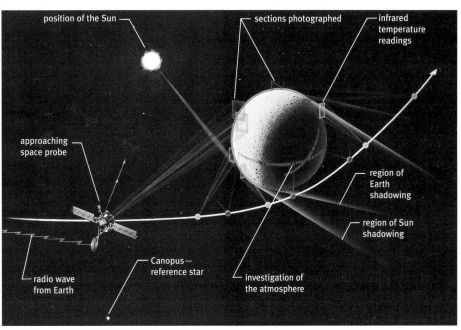

position of the Sun — / sections photographed / infrared temperature readings / approaching space probe / region of Earth shadowing / region of Sun shadowing / radio wave from Earth / Canopus— reference star / investigation of the atmosphere

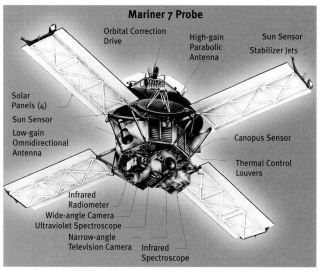

Mariner 7 Probe

Orbital Correction Drive

High-gain Parabolic Antenna

Sun Sensor Stabilizer Jets

Solar Panels (4)

Sun Sensor

Low-gain Omnidirectional Antenna

Canopus Sensor

Thermal Control Louvers

Infrared Radiometer

Wide-angle Camera

Ultraviolet Spectroscope

Narrow-angle Television Camera

Infrared Spectroscope

The antenna also receives guidance signals coming from the Earth. The antenna is usually mounted on a robotic arm so that it can be aimed at the Earth.

A powerful attitude stabilization system is indispensable for a probe. During the long flight and at the probe's distant destination this is used to keep it properly oriented. The solar panels must be directed toward the Sun, and the antenna for data transmission towards the Earth, for example. Measuring instruments must be pointed directly at the planet and at the specific sites researchers previously selected for investigation. The attitude stabilization of a space probe is achieved by using small steering jets that are attached to the central body. These mini-rockets are fueled by hydrazine. This is stored in a special tank under high pressure. Reference points for determining and correcting the probe's position

are the Sun and a bright star. The course is constantly checked relative to these points. Today there are also star mappers, which compare a star map stored in computer memory with stars they observe. From this they can compute flight coordinates. If a star mapper determines there is a discrepancy between the present orientation and the predetermined course, the guidance computer orders a corrective boost with one or more of the small hydrazine jets. For the more involved braking maneuvers that throw the probe into its orbit around the planet, the probe has a special engine.

Finally, space probes are outfitted with a powerful orbital correction system, which compensates for any imprecision in the flight trajectory to the destination planet. A small rocket engine gives the necessary correctional impulses. The fuel for this engine is stored in its own special tanks. The new orbiter probes combine both orbital correction and attitude stabilization into one system.

A PROBE'S INSTRUMENTS frequently include an infrared and ultraviolet spectroscope. These are used to determine the chemical composition and the dampness of Mars' soil, and also to identify the elements in the atmosphere and measure their density and temperature. Most probes also have a magnetometer on board to register magnetic fields and the radiation belts they are associated with. Often there is an instrument that detects small meteorites. Occasionally probes have special antennas to pick up cosmic radio waves.

Space probes have limited energy reserves and transmission power. They also cover very long distances on their interplanetary journeys. Control centers on Earth can only maintain **RADIO CONTACT** with space probes by using very large and sensitive antenna dishes. To support its many planetary probe missions, NASA has created the Deep Space Network (DSN), a network of antennas with diameters of 85, 110, and 225 feet. They are designed to detect even the faintest signals. DSN stations have been installed around the globe so that there is always one antenna turned in the direction of a given space probe, despite the Earth's daily rotation.

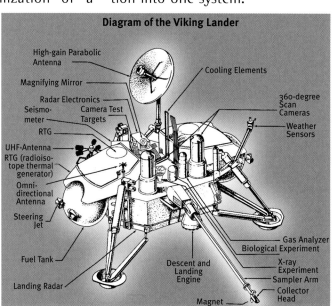

Diagram of the Viking Lander

High-gain Parabolic Antenna

Magnifying Mirror

Radar Electronics

Seismometer

Camera Test Targets

RTG

UHF-Antenna

RTG (radioisotope thermal generator)

Omnidirectional Antenna

Steering Jet

Fuel Tank

Landing Radar

Cooling Elements

360-degree Scan Cameras

Weather Sensors

Gas Analyzer Biological Experiment

X-ray Experiment

Sampler Arm

Collector Head

Descent and Landing Engine

Magnet

The Jet Propulsion Laboratory Control Center in Pasadena, California.

Everything is transmitted digitally. This means that every Mars photo is broken down into hundreds of lines and every line into hundreds of points or pixels. Each of these pixels reproduces one of 256 degrees of brightness, from white to gray to black.

These pixels are transmitted in the form of small "packets." Each packet contains a specific number of pixels. The beginning and the end of each packet is digitally marked and the packets are then transmitted to Earth one after another. When they reach Earth these "packets" are reassembled into the original picture.

How do the measurements and readings get to Earth?

Since space probes don't return to Earth, all of their scientific findings and all of their photographs have to be transmitted back to Earth, and the rate of transmission is very important.

The smallest unit of information in a digital transmission is a bit. In 1965 it took Mariner 4 more than 8 hours to transmit one picture, at a transmission rate of 8.3 bits per second (bps). The Viking probes were capable of transmitting 16,200 bps, and it only took a few minutes to send a picture.

This large antenna in California measures 225 feet across.

What results did Mariner 4 send back?

Toward the end of 1964, NASA launched its first two probes to Mars. Mariner 4 was launched on November 28, 1964 in an Atlas-Agena rocket. It was the only one of the two probes to survive launching and make it to Mars. In the summer of 1965, after a 6-month flight, it began transmitting spectacular close-ups of the surface of Mars back to researchers on Earth.

On the 14th of July, 1965 Mariner 4 flew past Mars at a distance of about 6,000 miles from the planet and produced 16 usable photographs encompassing about one percent of the planet's surface. To their surprise, scientists who examined the photos found about 70 impact craters ranging from 3 to 75 miles across, and also mountain ranges and regions covered with hoarfrost.

Mariner 4 also confirmed that Mars has very low temperatures and a thin carbon dioxide atmosphere—as scientists on Earth had already predicted. It wasn't able to detect a magnetic field around the planet.

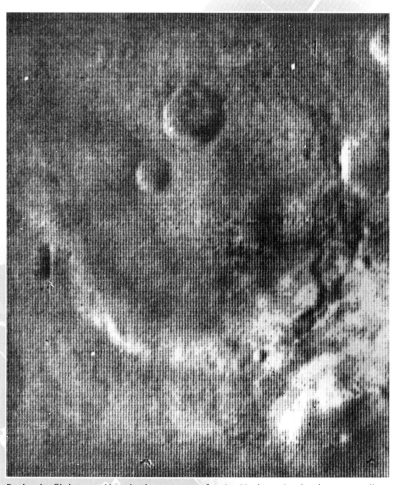

During its flight past Mars in the summer of 1965, Mariner 4's simple camera discovered dozens of large and small meteorite craters on the planet's surface. The existence of these impact craters on Mars was a great sensation at the time, since previously scientists had only seen such craters on the Earth's moon. Scientists were also surprised by indications of ice deposits and cloud cover. They were able to see all this despite the relatively coarse grain of the photographs.

The first American space probe to Mars weighed 575 pounds (260.8 kg), was 10 feet (3 m) tall, and had a wingspan of about 15 feet (7 m). The four solar panels produced only 200 watts, about the amount needed for two powerful light bulbs. The instruments on Mariner 4 were still very simple, and the most important one was the small camera.

Four Earth years—or two Mars years—after their success with Mariner 4, NASA sent two more probes to the Red Planet. The double launch—on February 24th and March 27th of 1969, using Atlas-Centaur rockets—went off perfectly this time. With an improved combination of technical equipment and measuring instruments the two new electronic explorers were supposed to coax new secrets out of the Red Planet.

Mariner 6 and 7 were considerably larger and heavier than Mariner 4 was. When they reached Mars, their four solar panels produced 370 watts of electrical power for the operation of the many instruments. At launch the probes weighed 910 pounds (412.8 kg) including all instruments. The scientific instruments weighed 127 pounds (57.6 kg). The communications system was capable of transmitting data at a speed of 16,200 bps—2,000 times faster than Mariner 4.

The central computer was pre-programmed with mission and back-up mission plans, but it could also be commanded and repro-grammed from Earth. A tape recorder with a storage capacity of 195 million bits stored television images. Mariner 6 and 7 were the first probes to have their instruments mounted on a 2-axis scan platform that could rotate to point the instruments in any direction.

Both probes had a wide-angle and a telephoto TV camera for wide-angle and close-up pictures of the surface of Mars. In addition there were three infrared and ultra-violet sensors that were used to analyze the chemical and physical properties of the surface and atmosphere of Mars.

WHY DID THEY ALWAYS LAUNCH TWO PROBES?

It takes years to prepare a probe mission, and the chances of success are about 100% higher when researchers launch two probes instead of one. If something goes wrong with a launch—as with Mariner 3—the remaining probe can still carry out the mission successfully.

Mariner 6 and Mariner 7 transmitted the first high-resolution close-ups of the surface of Mars. They showed a wealth of interesting details. The instruments on Mariner 6 explored primarily the southern polar cap and produced an entire mosaic of wide-angle and telephoto images of the icy craters and mountain landscape with its layers of frozen water and carbon dioxide. The individual photographs show segments of the surface about 1,000 miles wide and 100 miles wide. You can make out details measuring roughly 3,000 feet across in the larger ones and 300 feet across in the smaller ones.

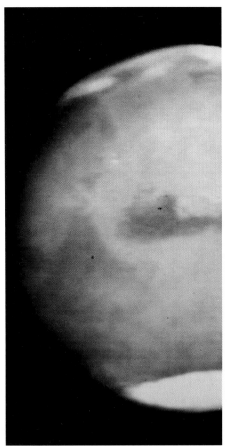

Mariner 9 sent us the first color pictures of the Red Planet—a sensation at the time. At the center of this picture you can clearly see the formation called Sinus Meridianus. In the south the winter polar cap is visible, and in the north the extensive cloud cover over the pole. For this image the camera took three photos one after another, each with a different filter— blue, green, and red. From these three exposures ground control was able to produce a color photo. Since the probe could only transmit limited amounts of data, this time-consuming process was only used on rare occasions.

to the planet it took 24 more pictures, both telephoto and wide-angle—primarily of the regions along the equator. For the first time scientists had pictures of Mars that showed details of Mars' surface that were less than 700 feet across.

NASA launched Mariner 7 on March 27, 1969. As it approached Mars it took pictures of the planet's daily rotation. On August 5th it passed near the planet at a distance of 2,000 miles and took 33 pictures with the telephoto and wide-angle cameras. Many were of the area around the south pole. The ultraviolet and infrared spectroscopes also transmitted valuable information about temperatures on Mars and about the composition and water-content of its soil and atmosphere. Temperatures ranged from –6° F at the equator to –250° F at the south pole.

The sensational details of these Mars photos from Mariner 6 and 7 show many round meteorite craters ranging in size from about 1,300 feet across to 250 miles across. These formations are considerably flatter than the craters on our Moon and some have a mountain in the center. The largest crater caused by a meteorite impact is the gigantic Hellas Region, which is probably quite young, geologically speaking—a few hundred million years old.

NASA launched Mariner 6 on February 24, 1969 and it flew past Mars July 31, 1969 coming within 2,130 miles. Two days earlier the telephoto camera began taking pictures—a total of 50 images of Mars over the course of 41 hours. This provided a number of different views of the planet. During the hours when it was closest

> **How successful were the Mariner 6 and 7 missions?**

Why was Mariner 9 so important?

When Earth and Mars came into favorable positions again, two years after Mariner 6 and 7, NASA launched two more space probes. The new thing about this mission was that for the first time the probes were programmed to orbit Mars. They would circle the planet along different paths and scan it with better sensors. Again only one of the launches was successful—Mariner 9.

This probe was similar to the two previous Mars probes, but the dimensions were larger and the equipment improved.

Mariner 9 had an element its predecessors did not: mounted on its central frame were an engine and two propulsion tanks that would maneuver the probe into its orbit around Mars. In the orbit around Mars the four solar panels produced 500 watts of power. Mariner 9 was about 30 feet in diameter and about 7.5 feet high. At launch it weighed 2,200 pounds. The propulsion system made up 968 pounds of the total, and the scientific instruments weighed 139 pounds.

Data was stored on an 8-track magnetic tape that could hold up to 180 million bits. This is where the continuous stream of photographs was stored, as well as the data from all other scientific instruments. The central computer had a memory of 512 words, and was programmed with 95 different commands. This meant that scientists could control the probe from Earth, and that it could function for several days on its own without support from Earth.

Mariner 9 was the first American probe to enter into orbit around Mars. This picture shows the probe's orbit as well as the orbits of the two moons, Phobos and Deimos. Mariner 9's orbit was elliptical. In other words, it moved far out away from Mars at one end and fairly close to the planet at the other.

Mariner 9 arrived at Mars on November 14, 1971. At a precisely calculated time it fired its braking engine. This maneuver put the space probe into an elliptical orbit around the planet. The orbit's furthest point from the planet was 10,657 miles and the closest point was 746 miles. The duration of one orbit was 12 hours, and the inclination toward Mars' equator was 65 degrees.

As the electronic observer approached the planet, however, there was disappointment on the faces of some researchers on Earth. The first pictures hardly showed any detail on the surface of the planet. There was a dust storm raging in the planet's atmosphere. As a result, Mariner 9 wasn't able to take any pictures or readings for the first few weeks. For the time being controllers directed the probe's cameras at the two Moons of Mars. They transmitted the first close-ups of the two small moons.

After several weeks the storm subsided. Now the probe began its research work. Each day when the probe came closest to the planet, its cameras took about 25 wide-angle or telephoto pictures of a predetermined area. By the 27th of October, 1972 America's first orbiting probe had transmitted a total of 7,300 images of the surface of Mars in addition to the first detailed images of the two moons. The wide-angle photos showed details as small as 3,300 feet across and the telephoto images showed details as small as 330 feet across.

Researchers assembled these images into the first nearly-complete atlas of Mars—with a scale of 1:5 million. These images showed scientists that the surface of Mars was surprisingly varied. Close-ups of the two moons also showed researchers for the first time that the moons were irregular in shape and covered by craters and fissures—they looked like "space potatoes."

Mariner 9's wide-angle and telephoto cameras often took pictures of the same area at the same time. This led to some impressive results.
The overview and close-up images of the 373-mile wide giant volcano, Olympus Mons, attracted a lot of attention. After all, it is the largest volcano cone in the solar system. The pictures showed surprising geological details on its peak and on its deeply fissured slopes. It was thrown up in the course of countless eruptions many millions of years ago, and reached a height of 16.8 miles.

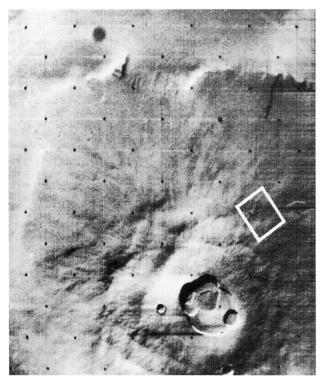

The Viking Mission— the First Landing on Mars

DATA ON THE VIKING PROBES:

Orbiter weight	2.26 tons
Lander weight	1.18 tons
Total Viking weight	3.44 tons
Height	19 feet
Wingspan of the solar panels	32 feet

What were the two Viking probes like?

The climax and close of the United States' first series of Mars probes was the Viking program, which launched two large, heavy instrument carriers. According to plan, once they entered orbit around Mars, each would send a capsule to the planet's surface. Many people now became interested in the question, whether or not life exists on Mars. Immediately after Mariner 9's success in the early 70's, engineers at the Jet Propulsion Laboratory (JPL) in California began building the Viking probes. They worked with contractors from private industry. The development of the two landing capsules was an entirely new technological challenge. No one before had ever built a probe that was meant to land on the surface of a planet and to carry out difficult analyses and measurements.

The base of the Viking orbiter was an octagonal ring just over 8 feet in diameter. The base held 16 modular compartments, and four solar panels extended out from it. In orbit around Mars they produced 620 watts of power. A parabolic dish antenna was mounted on one edge of the base. It also had a steerable scan platform. In the center was the rocket propulsion system that was to move the probe into orbit once it reached Mars. The Viking lander was enclosed in a protective shell and fastened to the bottom of the base.

At the heart of the Viking command system were two data processors, each with a 4,096-word memory that stored commands and also data that had been collected. This Central Computer and Sequencer (CC & S) controlled all of the orbiter's activities during the flight to Mars and the orbit around it. This made it possible for the orbiter to work independently—with all sensors operating—during its orbit around Mars. The most important functions could also be controlled from Earth using stored or transmitted commands.

The orbiter's instruments included three sensors. The Visual Imaging System had two identical 475-mm cameras and was programmed to photograph Mars systematically. The Infrared Thermal Mapper measured and recorded temperatures on Mars. Finally, the Water Vapor Mapper searched for water vapor in the soil on Mars and in the atmosphere—especially over the poles.

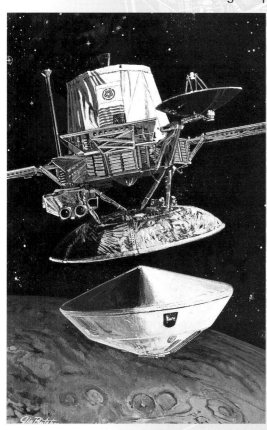

From this picture you can see that the Viking probes consisted of two basic elements: one that orbited the planet and one that landed on it. This drawing clearly shows the instrument platform, the propulsion system with braking rockets, and the antenna for communication with Earth. A relay antenna on one of the solar panels received data from the landers on the planet's surface.

Researchers pieced together 102 individual photographs to form this photo-mosaic of the hemisphere containing the giant canyon Valles Marineris and three large volcanoes. The Viking 1 orbiter took the individual photographs during February 1980. If you look closely, you can see several weather fronts in the area around the volcanoes, and in the south you can discern a number of small clouds. This was the first time scientists had seen such clouds. You can also clearly see craters of various sizes and a few prominent riverbeds.

For the first time engineers had to design a vehicle that could plunge through the atmosphere of a distant planet and make a soft landing

What difficulties were involved in building the Viking lander?

THE RADIOISOTOPE THERMAL GENERATORS that supplied electrical energy and heat are sometimes referred to as "atomic batteries." This is somewhat misleading. Although they use plutonium, they are not atomic reactors. These thermoelectric transformers make use of the natural decay of plutonium and convert the heat generated by this decay into electricity.

on its surface. Once it was on the surface it needed to be able to carry out sophisticated biochemical investigations and analyses. It was also important that the lander be sterilized before the launch, since scientists didn't want to carry any Earth organisms to Mars. They did not want to disturb the environment on Mars, and they also wanted to avoid contaminating the results of studies on Mars. Technicians solved the problem by heating the lander elements to more than 212° F (100° C). This killed any organisms on the components.

The Viking lander consisted of a six-sided aluminum base with alternating long (3.58 feet or 1.09 m)

and short (1.84 feet or .56 m) sides. It was 5.4 feet (1.65 m) across at the widest points. It rested on three extended legs attached to the shorter sides. The legs were equipped with shock absorbers to soften the landing. A hydrazine rocket provided propulsion. Two plutonium-driven radioisotope thermal generator (RTG) units supplied power. Three 6-nozzle engines, one attached to each long side of the base, were used for braking during descent and landing. Without fuel the lander weighed 1,300 pounds (590 kg). Scientific instruments made up 190 pounds (86 kg) of the total.

During the launch and the long flight, the lander was enclosed in a double capsule to protect it from the intense cold in space and the heat of its plunge through the atmosphere. A special heat shield helped brake its descent until a parachute system was activated and the braking rockets fired.

Located on top of the Viking lander's base are the cameras and other sensors and also the 3-foot (1 m) steerable parabolic antenna for data transmission. Extending out from the near side is the sampler arm, which collected samples and returned them to the testing instruments.

The scientific equipment carried by the Viking landers was extremely versatile and consisted of seven groups of devices. The most important instrument was the biological lab, which used three different processes to test soil samples for possible signs of life. In addition, the Viking landers were outfitted with devices to analyze the composition of the atmosphere and meteorological devices to monitor temperatures, wind speed and direction, and changes in atmospheric pressure in the course of the day or season. The Viking landers also had seismometers that recorded the intensity of planetary quakes.

What instruments did the Viking landers carry?

The two 360-degree scan cameras played an important role in the work of the Viking landers. They were equipped with various color filters and were adjustable to different focal lengths and degrees of resolution. They could make black-and-white images of the surroundings as well as color images and infrared or ultraviolet exposures. The best of the images transmitted back from Mars were so clear and sharp that an astronaut standing next to the lander couldn't have taken better ones. Stereo exposures made it possible to calculate precise distances between objects.

The Viking 2 lander took this picture of its surroundings while the sun was low on the horizon. In the foreground on the lander base you can see various devices with color scales on them and also the boom and part of the steerable antenna it supports. The reddish-brown rocks on the surface of Mars have a wide variety of shapes and sizes and are often full of large pore-like holes. The thin atmosphere of Mars has a pale pink shimmer.

The cameras on the Viking landers took fantastic pictures of the planet's surface. The parts of the lander in the foreground give you some sense of the spatial depth of the image. The sampler arm is in a raised position here. The camera's lens looks out over a sea of reddish-brown sand with many embedded rocks of all sizes and shapes. The furrows in the lower right corner of the picture show where the sampler arm has already taken soil samples for testing.

On August 20, 1975 NASA launched Viking 1 from Cape Canaveral on a powerful Titan-Centaur rocket. Precisely as scheduled, the Centaur upper stage rocket started the 3.4-ton space probe on its journey to Mars. Because of the tremendous mass, planners chose a path that was energetically favorable though rather slow.

On July 19, 1976 Viking 1 arrived at the Red Planet. At a precisely determined time the orbiter's rocket engine fired for about 45 minutes to brake the probe's speed enough so that the planet's gravity could pull it into orbit. The probe entered into exactly the orbit scientists had planned on, with a maximum distance from Mars of 19,263 miles and a minimum of 941 miles. The braking maneuver also established the orbit at the inclination to the Mars equator that

How did ground control guide the probes during flight?

scientists had hoped for—33 degrees—and at an orbiting time of 24.6 hours—exactly the length of one day on Mars.

Viking 1's first task after entering orbit was to examine possible landing sites. The sites had been chosen based on information from photographs taken by Mariner 9. These photographs didn't show sufficient detail, however, so the superior cameras of the Viking orbiters were used to inspect the sites once more before sending the landers to the planet. Ground control was unpleasantly surprised. The original choices for landing sites were much more uneven and rocky than scientists could have predicted from the Mariner images. The danger of a crash landing was so great that scientists had the Viking cameras scan the surface for more suitable sites. The cameras had already been prepared for such a possibility and they searched the areas along the equator according to a predetermined plan.

For the United States' first two Mars missions involving landings, safety had absolute priority over all scientific expectations. In the end, ground control chose two landing sites that lay relatively low in former riverbeds and were not too rocky.

Once researchers had decided on the destinations, they prepared for the descent of the first lander. On July 20, 1976, at a precisely calculated point in orbit, the lander separated from the orbiter and plunged down into the thin Martian atmosphere. Given the high speed of entry—3 miles per second—the aerodynamic resistance of the atmosphere was immediately felt and began slowing the capsule. A special protective shell deflected the heat generated by this resistance so that the sensitive instruments wouldn't be damaged. When the capsule had been slowed to the speed of sound, the parachute system was employed and the capsule slowly sank downward. Shortly before it reached the planet's surface, the lander's three descent and landing rockets fired and gently lowered the module onto the predetermined site on the surface of Mars.

On July 20, 1976, exactly seven years after the first manned Moon landing by Apollo 11, scientists at JPL Ground Control received the first images of the surface with tremendous enthusiasm. Over the next four years—until late 1980—Viking 1's two special cameras transmitted around 2,300 pictures.

The crater region at the peak of the gigantic Mars volcano Olympus Mons is 50 miles (80 km) across. It consists of several cooled crater beds that formed following a number of different eruptions. The Viking 1 orbiter took the 13 pictures used in this mosaic. They have a resolution that shows details as small as 65 feet (20 m) across. You can clearly see how sharp they are from this photo. Even with such clear pictures, however, it is hard to tell that the ridges of the craters are up to 1.8 miles (3 km) high. Scientists can calculate the height from the length of the shadows and the height of the Sun when the pictures were taken. The rocky walls generally have slopes with an angle of 30° or more. If you look closely at the picture you can also see signs of landslides on the crater walls.

For several years prior to the Viking missions researchers on Earth had been asking themselves a number of fundamental questions. In order to carry out experiments it was important to predict what life or microorganisms on Mars might look like. They had long ago given up any image of intelligent green men. But what are the possibilities for the development of life on other planets—planets whose historical development led to an entirely different environment than the one we know on Earth? Since we can't really imagine what life on other planets might look like, scientists decided to plan experiments to look for Earth-like life forms.

What were the results of the biological experiments?

The biological experiments were planned so that they could detect either microscopic life forms or by-products of the metabolic processes taking place in such life forms. Metabolic products are substances that all living beings on Earth excrete when they breathe, absorb nutrients, grow, or move.

First, scientists sent computer commands from Earth instructing the sampler arm to gather soil samples and place them in a distributor chamber. In the biological combination lab there were three different experiments that were carried out on the samples.

The pyrolysis (heat) experiment attempted to show the presence of life forms that carry on photosynthesis and absorb carbon dioxide—life forms like our plants.

The two metabolic experiments involved adding a nutrient solution to the samples. If organisms were present, they would consume the nutrients and analysis would show metabolic by-products. There were two experiment chambers, one for solid and one for gaseous by-products of metabolism.

The results of all the experiments from both Viking probes were confusing. There were reactions, but scientists weren't able to tell for sure whether they really came from microorganisms or not. The chemistry of Mars' soil was still unknown, and scientists couldn't rule out the possibility that the dead, inorganic soil might have caused the reactions.

The disappointment of the scientific community resulted in a 20-year interruption between the Viking missions and the next Mars probes NASA launched. For the time being scientists directed their attention to the exciting Voyager program and its two probes that were to investigate the outer planets: Jupiter, Saturn, Uranus, and Neptune.

The 3 analysis chambers, their electronic controls, and the extensive accessories for the biological experiments had to be fit into a very small space. Technicians and engineers worked for years to get the necessary elements small enough so that the entire laboratory wouldn't be any larger than a small cube about 1 foot long on each side.

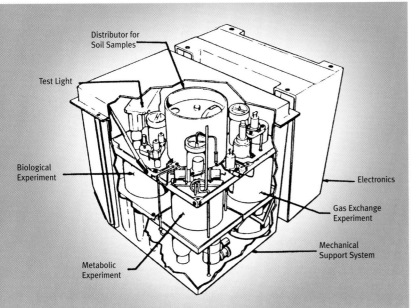

Distributor for Soil Samples

Test Light

Biological Experiment

Metabolic Experiment

Electronics

Gas Exchange Experiment

Mechanical Support System

This collage of images shows the Russian space probe Mars 96 as it would have appeared in orbit around Mars. Mars 96 didn't leave Earth's atmosphere, however. Due to a rocket failure the probe crashed into the Pacific. The Russians have not launched another Mars probe since then.

The Soviet Mars Probe Program

What did Soviet Mars probes look like?

Toward the end of the 1950's, Soviet space engineers began working intensively on the construction of lunar and planetary probes. Although the Soviets and the Americans were both interested in planetary research, they developed very different concepts for their space probes.

From the beginning, the Americans designed their probes with sophisticated computer systems that made them capable of functioning independently. They were also designed so they could be reprogrammed during the course of the mission. This made it possible to respond to unforeseen problems. Soviet Venus and Mars probes were relatively inflexible in comparison. They couldn't delay landing when conditions on or around the destination planet suddenly changed—when an unexpected dust storm arose on Mars, for example.

Starting with ZOND 3, which was launched in late 1965, Soviet Mars probes were divided into transport vehicle and landing capsule. The simple pictures published at the time showed the following construction: a cylindrical body measuring about 5 feet (1.5 m) in diameter and 12 feet (3.6 m) in height contained all of the probe's essential operating systems. This included flight control, attitude stabilization, communications, data storage, temperature regulation, and of course the scientific instruments. The landing capsule was fastened to the top of this cylinder and consisted of the actual instrument carrier and a surrounding protective shield that looked a lot like a "flying saucer." On the sides of the central body there were two large directional antennas for the exchange of data and two solar panels for energy production.

THE FIRST PROBES took all their pictures on regular photo film. The film was then developed and fixed inside the central body. Then a narrow beam of light scanned the negative and the different gray values were transmitted to the Earth in the form of radio signals. Later the Soviets too began employing more efficient television and video cameras on their planetary probes. This made it possible to process images digitally.

The **SCIENTIFIC EQUIPMENT** of the Mars landing capsules consisted primarily of an electronic camera for panoramic shots of the area surrounding the landing site. This was supplemented by a mass spectrometer for the detection of gases in the atmosphere around Mars and by several devices for chemical analysis of the soil. From an early date Soviet technicians worked together with experts from France and from several East Block countries on the instrumentation of their planetary probes. Chemical batteries provided the landing capsules with electricity, but they were usually exhausted after a few hours or days. Pictures and readings were transmitted to Earth via the orbiter, since its large solar panels gave it enough power for such data transmission.

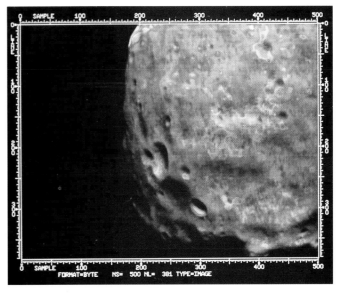

This photograph of the moon Phobos was made using different-colored filters. This technique reveals differences in the structure and composition of the planet's surface.

What instruments did the Soviet Mars probes carry?

Half of the total weight of a Soviet Mars probe —and NASA's Mariner 9 and Viking probes were no different—was the fuel the probes needed to put themselves into orbit around the planet.

The most important instruments on the probes were cameras with different focal lengths, ultraviolet and infrared sensors, and radiometers or spectrometers for analyzing the composition of the soil and atmosphere of Mars. Soviet plans also included investigating the two small moons, recording temperatures, and scanning for possible magnetic fields or radiation belts.

The landing capsules of the Soviet Mars probes were similar to their successful Moon probe Luna 9. Luna 9 was spherical in shape and opened up on the planet's surface like a flower bud blossoming. Four segments of the sphere's surface folded down and exposed the scientific instruments and the antennas for the link with Earth.

The landing capsule and central body separated two days before they reached their destination. The heat created as the lander plunged through the thin atmosphere around Mars was deflected by a special protective shield. Once speed had been reduced to around 300 mph, a parachute opened and the landing capsule drifted down to the surface. A small rocket engine that was activated by radar sensors fired to break the force of the final impact.

At first, Soviet space technicians launched space probes from their space station in Baikonur (Kazakhstan) every two or four years—depending on the relation between the positions of Earth and Mars. To launch the 3.4-ton Mars probe they needed their large Proton rocket. During the launch window in the summer of 1973 they launched four Mars probes one after another—an amazing organizational achievement.

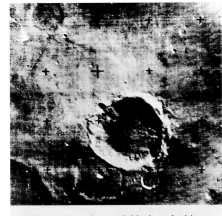

Soviet Mars probes took black-and-white photos of the planet's surface but the quality was not very good. All told, they were not able to make a complete atlas of the Mars like the one produced using images from Mariner 9 and the Viking orbiters. The crosses on this photo taken by a Russian probe are calibration marks made by the camera to make it easier for researchers to get exact measurements of the area in the photo.

Why did so many Soviet Mars missions fail?

Unfortunately Soviet scientists weren't very successful in their efforts to explore the Red Planet. Not a single landing capsule was able to transmit usable pictures of the surface or data about the atmosphere. The 8 orbiters of Soviet space probes launched prior to 1973 transmitted very few photographs and little data about the planet. Even the three probes built during the 1990's in cooperation with other nations failed tragically. Many people have speculated on the causes of this run of bad luck, since the Soviet Union's Venus probes were much more successful, despite a few problems in the beginning.

The two probes launched in 1971, Mars 2 and 3, may have been foiled by the violent dust storm in the atmosphere of the Red Planet—the same storm that kept the American probe Mariner 9 from its scientific work for several weeks. This hurricane on the surface of the planet may have destroyed the landing capsules or perhaps simply tipped them over before they could open.

The American space probes could be reprogrammed in such cases and put on hold, but the Soviet space probes didn't have this capability. Their Mars probes were set on automatic pilot and had to land on Mars at the predetermined time even if it meant their destruction.

After the four probes launched in 1973 also failed, the Soviet Union cancelled its Mars program for the time being and turned their attention to Venus. It wasn't until 15 years later that they made another attempt at exploring the Red Planet using space probes.

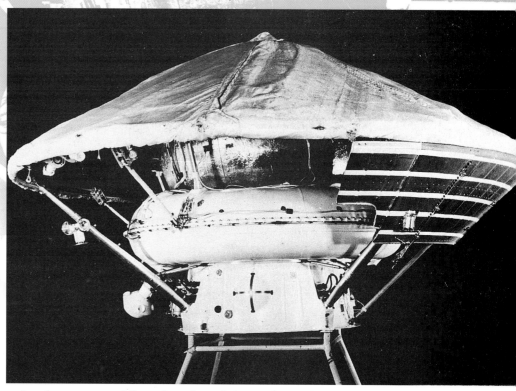

Like the Americans after the Viking program, the Soviet Union suspended its efforts after their first and largely unsuccessful series of Mars probes (1962-1973). Instead they now worked on improving their research methods and developing new instruments. The results of this reassessment were the two Phobos probes launched in 1988. As the name implies, they were primarily intended to study the larger of Mars' two moons.

The landing capsules of Soviet Mars probes were about 5 feet in diameter and shaped like tightly closed buds. They contained research instruments inside. During the plunge through Mars' atmosphere at a speed of 9,300 mph the landing capsule had to be protected from the tremendous heat the descent generated. Once it slowed to the speed of sound a parachute was activated and the capsule drifted down to the surface. A small rocket engine slowed it to soften the final landing jolt. It then unfolded like a budding flower.

What were the Phobos missions like?

Phobos 1 was sent off on its way to Mars on July 7, 1988 from Baikonur launch center. It was carried by a Proton rocket. Phobos 2 followed on July 12, 1988. Technical and human failures led to a premature end for the double mission, however. Only Phobos 2 succeeded in transmitting data, and this consisted only of a few pictures and instrument readings. There was great disappointment among Soviet researchers and their colleagues from other participating countries.

Researchers lost contact with Phobos 1 only seven weeks after launch, because the space probe received an incorrect signal from ground control. It changed its orientation, the solar panels no longer faced the Sun, and the big and wonderfully equipped probe froze to death. Ground control didn't recognize the danger in time to intervene.

On January 29, 1989 Phobos 2 reached Mars after a trouble-free flight. It transmitted its first images and also various scientific data from Mars and Phobos, and scientists were in good spirits. Before Phobos 2 could get close to the moon and launch its landing capsule, however, Soviet ground control lost contact with the probe—in March of 1989.

If the Phobos mission had gone as planned, it might have looked something like this artist's depiction. Various landing capsules were supposed to be shot down to the surface of Phobos. According to recent information the upper layers of its surface may consist of dark, carbon-rich dust.

Despite the bitter disappointment with the two Phobos probes, Russia planned to send off two more research

| **What happened to the Russian probe Mars 96?** |

spacecraft to the Red Planet during the favorable launch window in 1994. Again they invited numerous scientists and institutes from other countries to participate in the program. Because of political upheaval in the regions of the former Soviet Union, however, and because of financial problems, the new Mars project was postponed for two years, to 1996. They also cancelled one of the two probes.

The Russians themselves and also many participating technicians and scientists from around the world placed all their hopes in this big, new Mars mission. Thanks to the enormous load capacity of the Proton rocket, the probe was able to include about two dozen scientific instruments.

On November 16, 1996 the huge Proton rocket lifted off on schedule from the Russian launch site Baikonur. It soared into the night sky without any sign of problems. A while later, however, when the upper stage was supposed to fire again to move the probe into its flight path, ground control couldn't get any confirmation. Mars 96 sank into the Pacific only a few hours after its launch. Since this time planetary researchers around the world have concentrated their efforts more intensely on the new American space probes.

If Mars 96 had been successful, this camera would have produced 3-dimensional images of the planet's surface.

Germany contributed two special cameras to the Russian Mars 96 mission. Each of the cameras had different focal lengths and spectral ranges. They were supposed to transmit stereoscopic pictures that would have made it possible to create a precise three-dimensional topographic map of the entire surface of Mars.

An observer looks very small next to the huge Russian space probe Mars 96. The propulsion module forms the base of the probe, and includes several fuel tanks for the boost into orbit around Mars. Above this module is the central structure. All of the operating systems and scientific instruments are incorporated into this section. The two large solar panels are folded up for the launch. Beneath these panels are the two landing capsules and behind them you can see a part of the parabolic antenna. At launch the space probe weighed more than 6 tons.

NASA's New Mars Probes

This drawing shows one of the future Mars probes now in planning at NASA. It is supposed to enter into an orbit around the two poles and regularly pass over both northern and southern ice caps. As it does so it will monitor changes in the two ice caps from season to season. What interests scientists most is how the carbon dioxide ice cap regularly melts and then forms again, and also how the thinner layer of frozen water underneath behaves. Until now researchers could only observe these processes for brief periods of time and from an unfavorable perspective. In addition, thin layers of haze and clouds of ice crystals often obscure the polar regions.

Why are Mars researchers interested in the Antarctic?

For a long time, NASA was unable to get funding for new missions to Mars to follow up on the two Viking probes. According to NASA's previous strategy, a new mission would need to be even larger and more interesting than the previous project. Technicians discussed what a probe might look like that would have the ability to collect rocks on Mars and return them to Earth. Such a project would have cost several billion dollars, however, and this was more than NASA's budget could handle.

In the meantime several scientists were analyzing results from the Mariner and Viking missions. They carried out laboratory experiments that they hoped would make it easier to understand the confusing results of the chemical and biological investigations of Mars' soil. Other researchers undertook expeditions into the Antarctic and similar remote regions. There they studied the development of simple organisms under extreme climatic conditions—such as might have existed ages ago on Mars, when the atmosphere was denser and the temperatures higher.

During these research trips scientists also searched the glaciers of the South Pole for meteorites—rocks from outer space that are preserved in the eternal cold and protected from erosion. In 1984, during an expedition sponsored by the American Science Foundation, researchers discovered a potato-sized rock in the Allan Hills ice fields. It weighed about 4.4 pounds and was labeled as ALH-84001. They packed it in dry ice and stored it in nitrogen at the Antarctic Meteorite Center.

ALH84001,0

Researchers working in the Antarctic found this meteorite—Mars rock ALH-84001.

What's so unusual about Mars rock ALH-84001?

It wasn't until 1993, nine years after it was found, that scientists in the Lunar and Planetary Laboratory of NASA's Johnson Space Center in Houston, Texas finally examined the rock more closely. What they discovered was that the rock came from Mars and had grown very hot and then cooled off again several times. Ages ago this rock traveled a long and interesting path to get to Earth and came to rest in the Allan Hills after it passed through the Earth's atmosphere.

Using the data gathered by the Viking probes about rocks on Mars, scientists were able to determine the origins of other pieces of rock. They discovered that twelve more meteorites in their collection were from Mars.

Meteorite ALH-84001 is particularly unusual since analysis has shown that it is about 4.5 billion years old. This is four times as old as any of the previously identified Mars rocks found on Earth. Its age alone made it interesting to scientists, and they therefore examined it more closely than any of the other meteorites.

This examination led to a surprising discovery, which NASA announced at a press conference in Washington, D.C. on August 7, 1996. The experts claimed that they had found fossilized traces of minute life forms in this Mars meteorite. What they had found were tiny structures shaped like tubes or eggs, structure that can be interpreted as the remains of microbes. These miniscule life forms, if they really are such, are extremely small—100th of the thickness of a human hair—and can only be identified with an electron microscope.

These three researchers stand in front of the electron microscope they used to examine the now famous chunk of meteorite.

This is what the unusual tubular forms look like under an electron microscope. Scientists are still debating their significance even today.

The examination of this mysterious **MARS ROCK** and the discussion among scientists have not yet come to an end. The arguments of advocates and opponents of the microbe theory balance each other out so far. A new investigation of the rock in question has recently strengthened the position of the doubters, however. According to the new study, the structures that look like ancient, fossilized life forms could also have been created by natural geological processes on the planet.

How did the Mars rock get to Earth?

Through incredible detective work scientists have reconstructed the path that Mars rock ALH-84001 followed on its way to Earth. According to their theory the rock was created out of flowing, red-hot volcanic matter about 4.5 billion years ago during the formation of our solar system. Gradually the flow cooled and hardened.

Some experts believe these orange-colored structures and their chemical composition were formed by bacteria-like organisms.

Meteorites colliding with Mars heated up the rock again and caused cracks in its interior.

In the time between 4 billion and 3.6 billion years ago, so scientists assume, the atmosphere on Mars was considerably more dense than it is today and the temperatures were relatively warm. Experts now think that the presence of water and carbon dioxide may have fostered the growth of mini-microbes in the many cracks in the rock. About 16 million years ago another large meteorite collided with Mars and in the process blew many small pieces of rock into the air with such force that they were hurled out of the planet's gravitational field and entered into the free space between the planets.

About 13,000 years ago, after having circled the Sun many thousands of times in an ever smaller spiral, Mars rock ALH-84001 must have come near the Earth and have penetrated its atmosphere. Once again it was heated to a very high temperature. The piece of rock landed on the Antarctic continent and was preserved by the cold there. While looking for traces of Mars in remote regions scientists found the rock there.

The discovery of possible life-signs in the Mars rock resulted in heated discussions among specialists—and also among interested lay persons. Some experts believe the traces found in rock ALH-84001 are remains of very old, simple life on Mars. Others doubt this interpretation of the details observed in the rock and think that these tube- and egg-shaped structures originated on Earth or are remains of inorganic processes.

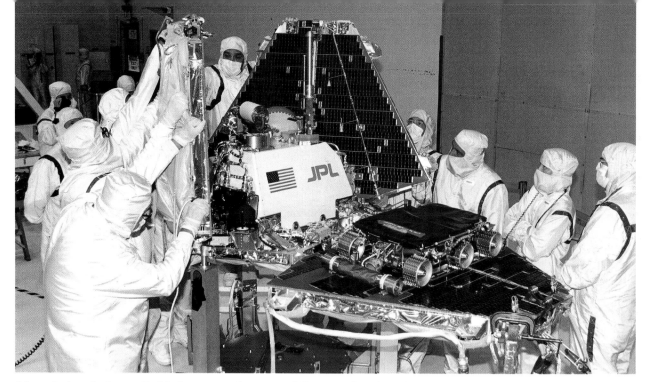

Prior to its launch, the new Pathfinder space probe was carefully mounted on the Delta carrier rocket. The three solar panels or "petals" were folded up so the entire assembly would fit under the protective cover. When technicians mounted the small six-wheeled rover on one of the three panels, they collapsed its top platform so the vehicle would fit when the panel was closed.

The discovery of the mysterious traces in Mars rock ALH-84001 —traces some people interpret as Mars microbes—was a stroke of luck for American space politics. Vice President Al Gore personally authorized NASA director Daniel Goldin to expand the research program for planetary probes, especially for probes to the planet Mars.

Within the framework of NASA's new Pathfinder program researchers developed a new landing capsule that would deposit a small all-terrain vehicle on the planet. They planned for it to examine the rocky surface of Mars over a longer period of time, using video cameras and a special chemical analysis device. In the meantime the lander would observe the atmosphere and weather on Mars and take panoramic photographs

What new space probes did NASA develop?

of the surrounding area. Scientists from other countries were also invited to participate in the project.

Mars Pathfinder consisted of a landing station with a mini-rover enclosed within. Both elements were packed in a protective shell during the launch and the many months of their flight to the Red Planet. The transfer stage had a rocket engine for attitude stabilization and course correction. A large antenna maintained contact with the Earth. The 16-square-foot solar panels provided electricity, producing 178 watts.

When it arrived at Mars, the probe immediately plunged into the atmosphere. It then braked until the parachute system was activated. Then the capsule slowly drifted toward the surface. A system of five huge airbags softened the landing. As the gases that inflated the airbags were released, the system assured that the capsule ended up in an upright position.

In comparison to the Viking probe launched 20 years earlier, the new **MARS PATHFINDER** was rather modest. The lander and the rover designed to explore the terrain surrounding the landing site fit together in a relatively small space.

The lander and the mini-rover were both contained in a conical protective capsule that protected them from the coldness of space during their long flight, and from the heat generated from friction while the probe entered into the atmosphere. After the landing this shell was cast off.

THE WEIGHT OF MARS PATHFINDER at launch was about 1,920 pounds. The rocket's upper stage and its fuel made up 670 pounds of this total—including about 175 pounds of hydrazine for the navigation system. When the probe entered the atmosphere of Mars it weighed 1,250 pounds; when the lander arrived on the planet it weighed only 715 pounds. The scientific instruments and the small rover weighed 35 pounds each. The rover's instruments weighed less than 10 pounds.

How was Mars Pathfinder equipped?

The construction of the Pathfinder probe is somewhat like earlier Soviet Moon probes. Both had a central core protected during transit by panels or "petals" that folded up over it. After it landed on Mars, Pathfinder lowered the three triangular panels, exposing the research instruments within. The base was barely one meter across and held all the important systems needed for an extended research period on the cold surface of Mars.

Equipment included a small, specially designed camera, an antenna, and various temperature, weather, and wind sensors. Two of the outer panels were covered with solar cells to provide power for the lander. The small rover was attached to the third panel. It rolled down onto the planet's surface by means of a special ramp. Pathfinder's equipment also included a powerful navigational computer, a data storage system for scientific findings, and a powerful radio transmitter.

Researchers were particularly interested in the IMP camera (Imager for Mars Pathfinder), which was raised up on a small mast after the landing so that it would have a better view of the surroundings. This camera was developed in cooperation with scientists from the Max Planck Institute in Germany. It weighed 11 pounds and could take color and black-and-white images as well as panoramic and stereoscopic photographs of the area surrounding the landing site.

The weather and atmosphere station on Pathfinder was based on the sensors developed for the Viking probes 20 years earlier and continued the work of its predecessors. The station began taking readings while the lander was still in its descent toward the surface—readings of temperature and air pressure in particular. The sensor weighed 4.4 pounds and required only 3.2 watts of electrical power.

Immediately after the successful landing on Mars and after the lowering of the three protective panels, the IMP camera transmitted its first images of the surrounding sand and rock desert. Using these images ground control was able to check the position of the mini-rover. It couldn't leave its ramp until the light-colored airbag had been fully deflated and the path was free. For three months the Sojourner rover roamed around the stony desert near the landing site. The solar cells mounted on its 2.7-square-foot platform supplied enough electricity to power its operations.

NASA launched its new Mars probe from Cape Canaveral on December 4, 1996 on a Delta rocket with a special PAM

How successful was Path-finder's mission on Mars?

upper stage. The ascent of the probe and its entry onto the calculated path or trajectory to Mars went off without incident. The

The imaging system took a first panoramic shot of the landing site. It turned out to be a reddish sand and rock desert, just like the sites where the Viking landers had set down 20 years earlier. Pathfinder had touched down at the exact site planned for its landing, in a low region called Ares Vallis. It was only 12 miles from the center of the 62-by-125-mile ellipse chosen for

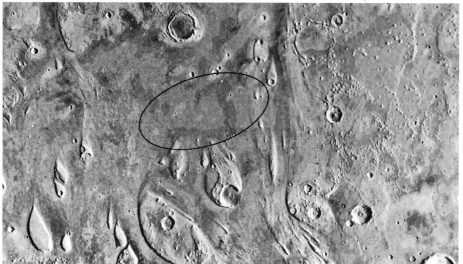

Pathfinder's landing site lies in a broad river delta where large quantities of water once flowed—billions of years ago. The terrain is low and relatively flat and promised interesting new information. It lived up to its promise, as researchers soon found out after the successful landing and activation of Sojourner. This photo-map is a mosaic made up of images transmitted by the two Viking orbiters 20 years earlier.

four course correction maneuvers performed while the probe was underway also went smoothly.

The scheduled day of arrival for Pathfinder was the 4th of July, the date of many important space exploration events. Thanks to ground control's precise navigation the probe arrived at Mars right on time, July 4, 1997. The capsule's entry into Mars' atmosphere, the aerodynamic braking that occurred as it passed through the atmosphere, the parachute descent, and finally the cushioned landing all went off successfully according to plan. Cushioned by four airbags, the lander bounced at least 15 times before it came to a rest. The airbags then deflated and Pathfinder opened its three triangular panels.

its landing. The exact coordinates of its position were 15° north and 160° west, about 530 miles southeast of Viking 1's landing site.

Planetary researchers around the world were ecstatic. They quickly forgot their disappointment over the loss of America's Mars Observer and Russia's Mars 96 probes. The success was particularly notable since NASA had planned Pathfinder only as a kind of demonstration of its new class of less expensive, simpler, and better planetary probes. The mission's goal was already achieved by the smooth landing. The months during which the lander and the rover were in operation on the planet were something of a bonus—one planners had hoped for but not necessarily expected.

Immediately after Pathfinder landed, ground control renamed it the "CARL SAGAN MEMORIAL STATION" in honor of the well-know researcher and author. He participated in the preparation of the project but died in late 1996 after a long illness— before the project was actually carried out.

Before it was launched, the small Mars rover was given the name Sojourner. Twelve-year-old Valerie Ambroise came up with the name as the winning entry in a contest NASA held for school children. She proposed naming the rover after the **ABOLITIONIST SOJOURNER TRUTH.** During the Civil War era this African-American woman worked for human rights and for equality for women.

One of the most important instruments used during the Pathfinder mission was the **IMP CAMERA** (Imager for Mars Pathfinder). It made a visual record of the area surrounding the landing site. To give it a better view, it was raised up on a mast to the height of 5 feet.

How did the mini-rover perform on Mars?

The most important part of the Pathfinder mission was probably the work of the small all-terrain vehicle. It wasn't much bigger than a remote-controlled toy car. The small rover's expeditions across the surface of Mars attracted a great deal of attention and enthusiasm both in the press and among the general population, which kept up-to-date on the mission via television coverage and the Internet.

The small vehicle was very simply constructed and equipped so that it could be active for a longer period of time in the inhospitable environment on Mars. With its six freely-suspended wheels it was capable of covering long distances. It could even surmount large rocks lying in its path. When it was completely unfolded for use, the vehicle was 2 feet long (63 cm), 1.6 feet wide (48 cm), and just under 1 foot high (28 cm).

The rover's top was a 2.7-square-foot platform covered with solar cells with a peak output of 16 watts. The small rover had to get by on this amount of power during its excursions on the cold planet.

The rover's navigation was semi-automatic, and was controlled via the small on-board computer. The computer was combined with a laser device that detected obstacles in the rover's path.

A navigation specialist on Earth monitored the rover's excursions using the black-and-white photographs that the vehicle was continuously transmitting back to Earth. The radio link with Earth was relayed through the Pathfinder lander.

There were two cameras, one on the front and one on the back end. The rover used these to keep its orientation in the rocky surroundings. The rover's most important instrument was its chemical analy-

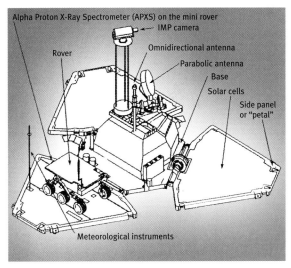

Alpha Proton X-Ray Spectrometer (APXS) on the mini rover
IMP camera
Rover
Omnidirectional antenna
Parabolic antenna
Base
Solar cells
Side panel or "petal"
Meteorological instruments

sis device, which had the complicated name Alpha Proton X-Ray Spectrometer (APXS). This "sniffer" was developed by American and European researchers and could analyze the chemical composition of rocks found at the landing site and was also equipped to detect any signs of ice on Mars.

The APXS weighed 1 pound and 16 ounces (740 g) and required only .8 watts of power for operation. The entire rover could get by on 13 watts, which is an amazingly small amount of power considering the difficult terrain the 6-wheeled vehicle had to cope with and all the scientific readings and measurements it gathered.

Front view of the mini-rover Sojourner. In the middle you can clearly see the cylindrical "sniffer" APXS.

The Pathfinder mission was extremely successful. It was initially planned to last only 30 days, but in 3 months of activity the "Sagan Memorial Station" and the Sojourner rover transmitted 3 gigabits of scientific data from Mars back to Earth. This was double what researchers had expected. The weather sensor alone took approximately 4 million temperature and wind readings.

The camera on the Pathfinder lander produced about 16,000 color and black-and-white pictures. The three cameras on the rover took an additional 550 pictures of the surrounding area. A photo sensor developed by the Max Planck Institute in Germany made it possible for the lander's camera to take infrared and ultraviolet exposures that revealed information about the atmosphere on Mars.

Over the course of 3 months the rover covered more than 330 feet and made a complete circle around the landing site. Directed by ground control, Sojourner steered toward several dozen rocks and examined them with its chemical analysis instruments.

Ground control had planned an excursion of the rover to a landmark some distance from the lander—two sandy hills they referred to as "Twin Peaks." They weren't able to carry out this excursion, however. Pathfinder's last successful transmission of data was on September 27, 1997. After a final radio signal on October 6th, however, the link to the Mars probe was broken permanently. The little Mars car probably continued functioning, but without the lander it couldn't communicate with Earth.

In addition to being a tremendous technological and scientific success, Pathfinder was also the world's biggest Internet event so far. As soon as NASA received pictures and data from Pathfinder, it posted many of these results on the World-Wide Web.

During the first 30 days after Pathfinder landed, the Pathfinder site on the **WORLD-WIDE WEB** was accessed over 500 million times. On July 8th alone, when the first surface images were made public, there were more than 50 million visitors to the site.

Control engineers gave nicknames to the largest objects in the "rock garden" surrounding the lander. In this picture the rover stands next to "Barnacle Bill," at the right-hand edge of the picture is "Yogi." Many of these rocks were examined closely by the small vehicle and its chemical analysis device.

NASA's Mars Global Surveyor probe is designed to survey and study the surface and atmosphere of the Red Planet over a long period of time. The instrument platform is steerable and will constantly face the planet. The large cylinder on top (in the photograph above) contains the high-resolution camera, which can pick up objects as small as 15 feet across. Two solar panels provide power, and a large antenna transmits instrument readings to Earth.

The "Face on Mars." It looks like it was made by Martians, but it is actually a naturally formed mountain.

under a ton. The camera and instruments made up 165 pounds of the total. The probe now orbits Mars once every 11.6 hours.

Aerobraking maneuvers will slowly lower the probe's orbit. Aerobraking means the probe drops into Mars' atmosphere from time to time. Friction caused by the atmosphere slows the orbiting speed and the altitude of the orbit drops. This process was interrupted for a year because of a defect in one of the solar panels. According to present plans the probe will reach its final orbit in spring 1999. It will circle the planet over the poles at a height of 228 miles. Each orbit will take 118 minutes.

Already in the first months the probe's instruments have transmitted their first data about the planet's surface and atmosphere. Scientists are very enthusiastic about the extremely sharp pictures it has sent back. They show objects as small as 15 feet across in extraordinary detail. Once the probe reaches its predetermined orbit, the camera will begin a 2-year surveying project to provide high-quality images of the entire surface of Mars. With these pictures cartographers will be able to produce a map of Mars with a scale of 1:100,000. This could be used to plan manned missions to Mars.

At present Mars researchers are analyzing the most recent pictures to find insights into geological, volcanic, and tectonic processes, and also to study water and wind erosion on the planet. These are the factors that formed the surface of Mars over the course of billions of years.

What does Mars Global Surveyor look like?

At the end of 1996 NASA launched a second probe along with Pathfinder, and in the fall of 1997 it entered an orbit around the Red Planet. Its mission was to study it from a low orbit. This probe, Mars Global Surveyor, consists of a cube-shaped core with 5-foot-long sides, two solar generators with a capacity of 1,000 watts, and an antenna. At launch the probe weighed just

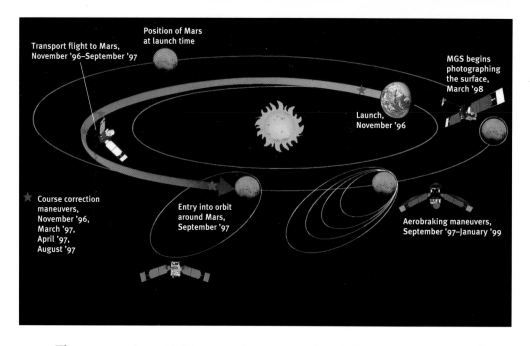

The camera's activities up to this point form a record of especially interesting regions of Mars, for example, of the Pathfinder landing site. The

What results has Mars Global Surveyor produced so far?

lander itself isn't visible in the pictures, since the resolution still isn't high enough to record such a small object. The more pronounced landmarks are all visible, however, just as recorded by Pathfinder's panoramic imaging system—the "Twin Peaks," for example.

Global Surveyor's telephoto camera has also photographed the well-known "Mars face" from a relatively close distance. On earlier Viking photos with lower resolution, this structure looks like a face and has provoked numerous discussions. Many saw it as an artificial structure left behind by intelligent inhabitants of Mars. In these excellent new images, however, the "face" is unmasked as a

normal plateau—about a mile long—located in the middle of the rocky Mars desert.

Mars Global Surveyor has also taken new pictures of Mars' larger moon—Phobos—and from a relatively short distance. The pictures are impressive. They show the 6-mile-wide Stickney Crater with its steep inner slopes.

Spectrometer analyses of Phobos show that temperatures on the sunlit day-side are about 25° F (-4° C) and that they rapidly sink during the 3.5-hour-long night (to -233° F or -112° C). These extreme temperature jumps are caused by a layer of dust on the surface. The layer is more than 3 feet deep and was formed by tiny rock particles that bombarded Mars over the course of billions of years.

The picture on the right was taken by Mars Global Surveyor and shows a plateau and surrounding steep slopes within the Valles Marineris, the giant canyon on Mars. The highest terrain is the relatively smooth plateau near the center. Slopes fall off to the north and south (upper and lower part of the picture) in broad, debris filled gullies with intervening rocky spurs. The left and center images were pieced together from photos taken by Viking probes.

New American and European Mars Space Probes

What is the mission of Mars Climate Orbiter?

Since the Pathfinder mission was so spectacularly successful, people are anxiously awaiting NASA's new Mars probes. Again NASA has planned an orbiter and a lander and given the pair the name "Mars Surveyor 1998." The two elements get lifted into space by a Delta rocket launched from Cape Canaveral.

Mars Climate Orbiter was launched successfully on December 11, 1998. After a flight lasting 9 months it will arrive at the Red Planet on September 23, 1999. There it will enter into an orbit around the planet's two poles. From this orbit the probe's instruments will be able to scan the entire surface once each day. The mission of MCO is scheduled to last at least two Earth years—one Mars year, that is.

The new Mars orbiter is built much like its predecessor, but it weighs only about half as much. The central frame contains the flight systems. Large solar panels and an antenna extend out from the sides. One particularly notable new feature is the camera, which weighs only a little more than a pound and has two lenses. One lens will produce pictures showing details as small as 130 feet across, the other lens will show details measuring as little as 6.5 feet across! Once a day the wide-angle camera will scan the entire surface of the planet and examine weather conditions in the planet's atmosphere. It will regularly monitor the movements of clouds and sandstorms. The infrared radiometer will monitor distribution and variations in temperature and also the composition of the atmosphere. It will also record carbon dioxide and water vapor levels in the atmosphere and also particulate count, especially over the polar caps.

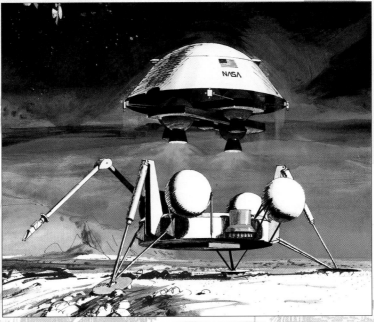

One of the future NASA Mars probes will collect rock and sand samples and bring them back to Earth. The base may have been modeled after the design of the Viking probes, and will serve as launch platform for the upper stage of this probe. The mission is planned for the year 2005. Engineers hope that new construction methods and advanced electronics will secure the success of this very difficult mission. The success of this mission is an important first step in the process of landing astronauts on Mars. The cost for NASA's newest double mission is estimated at 187 million dollars.

Mars Polar Lander is the second probe in NASA's latest double mission. It is scheduled for launch on January 3, 1999. After 11 months it will land on Mars. The lander is much like the Pathfinder lander: it has a central frame supported by legs extending from the base. Two large solar cell panels extending from the sides will supply power.

The MPL will be the first lander to try to set down near the south pole. Scientists don't expect to find traces of life here—it's too cold. So far all Mars landers have set down on or near the planet's equator. After the instrument capsule lands a stereoscopic camera will photograph the surroundings. The camera is similar to the one on Pathfinder that was so successful.

Another important element of this Mars probe is its sampler arm, which will collect soil samples and place them in a small lab where they will be more closely examined. If the probe lands directly in a snowfield it may be able to ana-

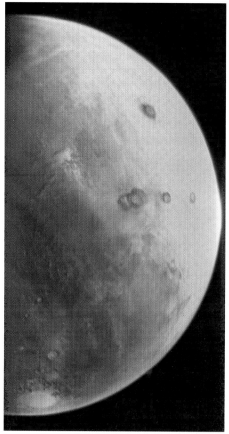

A Viking probe took this photograph of one side of Mars. The four large volcanoes on the Tharsis plateau are clearly visible, as are numerous mountain ranges, craters, light and dark regions, mists and clouds, and the southern polar cap.

lyze the chemical composition of Mars' southern polar cap directly.

When the lander begins taking readings, it will fire two small probes into the ground. They will analyze the soil. Various instruments will monitor the weather and atmosphere. A small microphone will record any sounds generated on the surface of Mars.

This is what the orbiter and lander of the Mars mission "Mars Surveyor 1998" may look like.

The Mars Express.

What plans does Europe have for building space probes?

For a long time probes of the United States and the Soviet Union—now Russia—have dominated Mars exploration.

Once in a while they took instruments from other nations along on their missions. Members of the European Space Agency (ESA) have long participated in international missions, but they are now plan-

The German Center for Air and Space Travel in Cologne is testing mini-rovers that carry a variety of instruments despite their small size. With only a small amount of power they can travel relatively large distances. Researchers are testing the first models for such minivehicles on a model of a section of Mars' surface. They thoroughly check its propulsion and navigation systems. These mini-rovers aren't just suited for Mars, however. They could easily be used on one of the large moons around Jupiter, for example.

ning Mars projects of their own to investigate specific questions not yet looked into by American or Russian missions. Some time ago the ESA announced plans for the Inter-Mars-Net. The project originally envisioned sending several small recording stations to the Red Planet. They were to be launched on an Ariane 5 rocket in 2003. Astrophysicists would like above all to investigate the interior of the planet and the way the planet was formed and has changed over time.

In the meantime the Inter-Mars-Net project has been re-

named Mars Express. An Ariane 5 rocket will carry several small landers that will be deposited on the surface of Mars. The research for Mars Express has provided a foundation for the development of a future network of scientific recording stations on Mars.

Each of the small recording landers will weigh only 16.5 pounds. They will regularly transmit their data to the orbiter that placed them on the planet, and the orbiter will relay them to Earth. ESA is also planning a larger landing station for more extensive surface investigations. The spacecraft containing the Mars Express mission components will weigh almost 2.5 tons. At present this project is only one of many being considered by the ESA. In the fall of 1999 the ESA will decide whether or not the Mars project will be among the plans it carries out.

The European Mars probe might also contain a small rover like the one carried on the successful Pathfinder mission—Sojourner. It is being developed by an institute in Cologne, Germany. According to present plans the rover will be only 2.75 inches high, 9.5 inches long, and 8.25 inches wide. It will use only a small amount of electricity and will have a very high degree of mobility.

When will humans fly to Mars?

In interplanetary terms, the distance between Earth and Mars is relatively small. Despite all differences between the two planets, conditions on Mars are nevertheless bearable for humans, and one day it will be possible for humans to land on the planet. There is no doubt about this. Today's space probe activities related to Mars are also designed to help prepare for a future manned flight to Mars.

For decades now scientists have been working on plans for manned flights. German-American rocket scientist Wernher von Braun prepared the first complete study in the 1950's. His work is the foundation for much recent research on the possibility of a trip to Mars. NASA, the Russians, and now the Europeans and the Japanese, all have plans in the works.

So far, however, the political will for a gigantic space exploration mission like this has been lacking—and the necessary money as well. For the moment space agencies are focusing on building and operating the International Space Station. This will consume the majority of space exploration resources for the next 15 to 20 years. It will take new and sensational reports about traces of life on Mars to raise support for a manned Mars mission. When this happens, the general public—and the politicians—will surely be quick to call for a manned Mars project.

It isn't possible to fly to Mars directly—it would take far too much energy to fly such a course. For this reason planners must choose a launch time when the two planets are in a favorable position relative to each other. The brief span of time during which the launch from Earth or the return from Mars must take place is called the **"LAUNCH WINDOW."** This

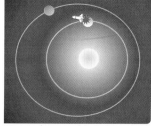

Manned spaceship is launched from Earth.

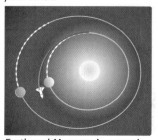

Earth and Mars are in opposition (when they are nearest to each other).

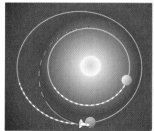

The spaceship lands on Mars.

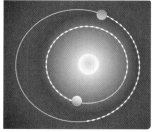

Earth and Mars are in conjunction (when they are farthest from each other).

There are many proposed designs for the spaceship that will one day carry the first humans to the planet Mars. At present we still don't have the necessary technology and logistical procedures, not to mention the money, for such an undertaking. At one point designers were considering a nuclear-powered engine for the long flight to Mars, but today planners are returning to conventional chemical rocket engines. The necessary electrical power for the operation of on-board systems will be generated by large solar panels, which still provide sufficient power even as far from the Sun as Mars is.

opportunity arises approximately every two years. The flight to Mars would take about 240 days (eight months). During a short mission the astronauts would then have about one month to carry out experiments. During a long one they would have about 550 days before they had to begin their return flight to Earth.

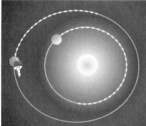

The spaceship takes off from Mars.

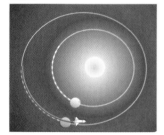

The Earth and Mars are in opposition.

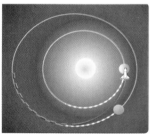

The spaceship lands on Earth.

The elliptical flight path from Earth to Mars and Mars to Earth is also called a **HOHMANN ORBIT**. German engineer Walter Hohmann calculated a possible flight trajectory for an interplanetary journey as early as 1925.

What would a manned Mars spaceship look like?

Engineers are now considering various options for space travel to Mars. One option would be to send the manned mission to Mars in several large rockets launched directly from Earth. Another option would be to establish a space station on Mars and launch the missions from there. Every option has its advantages and disadvantages, and these will have to be weighed against each other.

Specialists are also discussing whether there should be only one manned mission to Mars or if it wouldn't be better to launch several missions to Mars—like the Apollo flights to the Moon. The flights would have to be several years apart, however, since researchers on Earth would need to wait and see how the previous missions turned out.

In 20 or 30 years there will perhaps be new possibilities in rocket construction. A manned flight to Mars would certainly need one or possibly several carriers like the American Saturn 5 or the giant Russian rocket Energija. It would take a rocket of this type to take the heavy spaceships to their remote destination. It is thus sad that neither of these carrier systems is being built anymore.

We should be skeptical about new studies arguing for a pared-down manned flight. Experts say such a flight would cost only a few billion dollars. Experience with large international projects has often demonstrated that such things generally cost many times the original estimate, however.

A combined landing and launch stage for a manned Mars mission might look something like this. Astronauts would penetrate the atmosphere and set down on the surface in this ship, and would then lift off in the same ship at a later time and return to the mother ship in orbit around Mars. A manned flight to Mars will probably follow a very similar plan as the earlier Apollo missions did. The visit of astronauts on our neighbor planet will of course take much longer and will take the astronauts much further away from Earth. The crew of the Mars spaceship will be entirely on its own.

In addition to all the political, financial, and technological questions there are even more important human issues that must be addressed when planning a Mars mission that will last several years. Because of the unusual relationship between the planetary orbits of Earth and Mars a flight like this would take at least 456 days using currently available chemical rocket engines. This includes 210 days each for the flights to and from Mars. Only one month would be left for the stay on Mars under these conditions. The astronauts wouldn't have enough time for more extended activities on the surface of Mars. In order to provide a more extended research phase on the Red Planet a mission lasting at least 3 years would be necessary.

A flight lasting this long would place tremendous physical and psychological demands on the crewmembers of the flight. After about one year of weightlessness during the transport flight, the crewmembers would suddenly have to be top-fit when they stepped out onto the surface of Mars and began carrying out difficult and strenuous tasks. On the return trip they would once again spend a year in weightlessness. After they arrived on Earth the astronauts would again be exposed to full

Plans for a manned mission to Mars are at present still in the minds and computers of engineers. These plans also provide artists with information they use to give us views of what future Mars spaceships might look like. Among these artists' drawings is a design for a rotating structure that would create a degree of gravity for the astronauts during their long transport flight. This could help them stay strong for their arrival on Mars. Part of the equipment of a Mars spaceship is always a large rocket engine to speed the ship on its journey to and from the planet. Designers have had a hard time picturing the actual landing unit. It must include some kind of take-off and return stage to get the astronauts back to the mother ship.

Europeans recently published a new concept for a Mars probe. The numerous landers would use the thin atmosphere on Mars to brake their descent. This will require an effective heat shield to protect the landers from the heat generated by friction as they plunge through the atmosphere. For a mission where landers are supposed to return samples to Earth the technical demands and fuel quantities required are twice as great. When the lander takes off from Mars it has to overcome the planet's gravity before it can return to Earth.

of this kind. They would need extensive physical exercise on a regular basis while on board in order to be fully active when they arrive on Mars—even though the gravity there is only 40% of Earth's. As Russian space physicians report, bones and muscles grow weak under conditions of weightlessness if astronauts don't exercise regularly during long flights.

Scientists haven't yet succeeded in developing fully regenerating, self-replenishing supplies of basic requirements for life in the closed environment of a spaceship—and they aren't likely to succeed in the near future. A Mars spaceship would thus have to bring all the necessary supplies from Earth. This would include large quantities of nitrogen, oxygen, water, and food. Electrical energy could be generated continuously, however, using large solar panels. Even though Mars is far from the Sun, solar panels could still produce sufficient energy.

So far there is no medical, technological, or scientific evidence that would suggest a manned flight to Mars is categorically impossible. The dream of humans walking on the surface of Mars is ultimately within our reach.

Earth gravity and might well have serious problems as they adjust to the change.

So far Soviet or Russian cosmonauts have the most experience with long-term space flight. Several cosmonauts have stayed on the Mir station for one year or more and returned to Earth without lasting damage. In the view of many experts they have proven that even a 1.5-year or 3-year mission is possible from a biomedical perspective. Even so, crewmembers would have to be in above-average physical condition to withstand a strain

TABLE OF PLANNED MARS SPACE PROBES

Designation		Launch	Arrival	Mission goals
Planet B	(Japan)	July 1998	November 1999	Mars orbit
Surveyor 98	(USA)	December 1998	November 1999	aerobraking orbit; Mars mapping; transmission relays
Surveyor 99	(USA)	January 1999	December 1999	direct entry; south pole landing; soil samples
Microprobes	(USA)	January 1999	December 1999	placement of lander on Mars
Surveyor 01	(USA)	February 2001	January 2002	orbiter aerobraking; surface mapping
Surveyor 01	(USA)	March 2001	December 2001	direct landing in highlands with a 90-pound rover
Surveyor 03	(USA)	May 2003	February 2004	direct landing, collection of soil samples
Mars Express	(Europe)	May 2003	March 2004	orbiter with some of the experiments from Mars 96
Surveyor 05	(USA)	July 2005	April 2006	Earth-Mars-Earth; return with soil and rock samples

Mars Fact Sheet

THE PLANET MARS IN COMPARISON TO EARTH

	Unit of measure	Mars	Earth
Mean distance from Sun	million miles	141.58	92.94
Orbit period	days	686.98	365.256
Diameter (at equator)	miles	4,221.8	7,926.6
Mass (relative to Earth)	percent	10.7	100
Volume (relative to Earth)	percent	15	100
Surface area (relative to Earth)	percent	27.45	100
Surface gravity	m/s^2	3.69	9.78
Mean density	kg/m^3	3933	5520
Atmospheric pressure	mbar	3-8	1000
Inclination to orbital plane	degree	25.19	23.45
Length of day (rotation time)	hr:min:sec	24:37:23	23:56:04
Escape velocity	km/s	5.03	11.19
Number of moons		2	1

THE MOST IMPORTANT MARS SPACE PROBES

Designation		Launch Date	Arrival	Mission/Results
Mars 1	(USSR)	11/1/1962		failed in Earth orbit
Mariner 3	(USA)	11/5/1964		didn't attain Earth orbit
Mariner 4	(USA)	11/28/1964	7/14/1965	first successful flight past Mars; 22 photos of Mars surface
Zond 2	(USSR)	11/30/1964		probe failed after 5 months, missed Mars
Zond 3	(USSR)	7/18/1965		photographed moon, flew on to Mars, no data
Mariner 6	(USA)	2/24/1969	7/31/1969	2nd flight past Mars; 74 photos of equatorial region, instrument readings
Mariner 7	(USA)	3/27/1969	8/5/1969	3rd flight past Mars; 91 photos of southern polar region; instrument readings
Mariner 8	(USA)	5/8/1971		didn't attain Earth orbit
Mars 2	(USSR)	5/19/1971	11/27/1971	entered Mars orbit; transmitted data; Mars landing failed
Mars 3	(USSR)	5/28/1971	12/2/1971	entered Mars orbit; transmitted data; contact broke off after Mars landing
Mariner 9	(USA)	5/30/191	11/13/1971	entered Mars orbit; 7,329 photos; contact broke off on 10/27/1972
Mars 4	(USSR)	7/21/1973	2/10/1974	missed Mars orbit because of braking rocket failure
Mars 5	(USSR)	7/25/1973	2/12/1974	entered Mars orbit; transmitted data and photos
Mars 6	(USSR)	8/5/1973	3/12/1974	capsule landed; radio contact lost at landing
Mars 7	(USSR)	8/9/1973	3/9/1974	landing capsule missed the planet
Viking 1	(USA)	8/20/1975	6/19/1976	entered Mars orbit; lander set down on 7/20/1976; 37,000 photos from orbiter, 2,300 from lander
Viking 2	(USA)	9/9/1975	8/7/1976	entered Mars orbit; lander set down on 9/3/1976; 16,500 photos from orbiter, 2,250 from lander
Phobos 1	(USSR)	7/7/1988		Radio contact broke off on 9/2/1988
Phobos 2	(USSR)	7/12/1988	1/29/1989	entered Mars orbit; photos and data from moon Phobos; contact with probe lost on 3/27/1989
Mars Observer	(USA)	9/25/1992		Radio contact broke off on arrival at Mars
Mars Global Surveyor	(USA)	11/7/1996	9/11/1997	photo mapping of surface of Mars
Mars 96	(Russia)	11/16/1996		launch failed, landed in Pacific
Mars Pathfinder	(USA)	12/4/1996	7/4/1997	landed in Ares Vallis; Sojourner rover functions according to plan